NOT ZERO

Not Zero

*How an Irrational Target
Will Impoverish You, Help China
(and Won't Even Save the Planet)*

ROSS CLARK

FORUM

FORUM

First published in Great Britain in 2023 by Forum, an imprint of Swift Press Ltd

3 5 7 9 8 6 4 2

Copyright © Ross Clark, 2023

The right of Ross Clark to be identified as the Author of this Work has been asserted in accordance with the Copyright, Designs and Patents Act 1988.

Typeset in Bembo by Palimpsest Book Production Ltd, Falkirk, Stirlingshire

Printed and bound in Great Britain by CPI Group (UK) Ltd, Croydon CR0 4YY

A CIP catalogue record for this book is available from the British Library

ISBN: 978 1 80075 242 9
eISBN: 978 1 80075 243 6

Contents

1.

The conference of idle promises

IT BEGINS, LIKE A VICTORIAN melodrama, with a train, lashed by a Halloween storm, pulling to a halt in the English countryside. As the minutes turn to hours – a fallen tree has blocked the line – the increasingly restive passengers begin to converse, in this case via Twitter, and realise they are not random individuals; they are there for a reason. They are all travelling to the COP26 climate summit in Glasgow where the UK government, which is hosting the event, will try to convince the world to follow its unilateral example and legally commit to reaching net zero carbon emissions by 2050. And they begin to see their predicament through that prism. The global ambassador for a development charity opines that British public transport infrastructure is in a dire state. The President of the Federation of Austrian Industries is regretting that, having flown in to Heathrow from Mexico in the morning, he hadn't done as many of his fellow delegates had done and taken an onward jet to Glasgow.

But a storm is no longer allowed simply to be a storm; rather it is a portent of global doom. It is Jon Snow, the anchor on *Channel 4 News*, who catches the mood of the train as he tweets: 'En route to COP26 – trees and branches affected by climate change have slowed our rail journey – tho the branches have been cleared we are down to 5mph – What an irony! What a message! We MUST change! Dare we hope that we shall?'

The Earth is warming and there have been observed changes in the climate, and in sea levels, which pose problems for human societies. But to blame the storm that brought down the power lines on climate change is directly at odds with observational evidence presented in the Intergovernmental Panel on Climate Change's sixth assessment report – seen by many as the bible of climate science – published in August 2021. That cited evidence that the wind speeds over land throughout the northern hemisphere have been falling in recent decades. Moreover, the number of intense storms – those with a central pressure of lower than 960 millibars – in the North Atlantic have fallen sharply since 1990.[1] In other words, if climate change is having any effect on your chances of a rail journey in Britain disrupted by high winds it is to *reduce* them. Not to mention that the reason trees fall on railway lines in Britain more than they used to is that since the end of the steam train era, trees and bushes beside railway lines have been allowed to grow up in order to help with biodiversity. Network Rail even promotes the estimated 6 million trees which line railways in Britain as having a role in 'much-needed carbon capture'[2] – too bad if falling branches delay your train.

But these are details which get lost in the climatic hyperbole which surrounds the COP26 summit. The growing divide between the statements of campaigners who claim to have science on their side and what scientific data actually says goes unnoticed. In COP26 land it is accepted wisdom that mankind, along with the planet, is on the brink, and only drastic action will save us – no matter what the cost to society and to ordinary people. The summit's opening presentation quickly attains the air of an evangelical rally, with world leaders – many of whom having flown in hours earlier on gas-guzzling private jets, emitting between five and 14 times as much carbon as they would have done had they flown by commercial plane[3]

– trying to outdo each other in their doom-laden addresses. The then UK Prime Minister, Boris Johnson – who, six years earlier, wrote that the 'fear' of man-made climate change was 'without foundation' – expresses the zealotry of the convert by telling delegates that the world is now 'a minute from midnight'. The UN Secretary-General, António Guterres, announces that we are all 'digging our own graves' by failing to cut carbon emissions. Documentary-maker David Attenborough declares that humans 'are already in trouble'. The Prince of Wales, whom Johnson later calls a 'prophet', demands a 'vast, military-style campaign' to defeat climate change. But it is the Archbishop of Canterbury, Justin Welby, who outdoes everyone else by stating that failing to address climate change would 'allow a genocide on an infinitely greater scale' than the Holocaust – a comment for which he later apologises.

It gradually becomes clear, once the Archbishop has left his pulpit, that not everyone in the congregation quite shares the same devotion to the cause. US President Joe Biden arrives in a cavalcade of 21 vehicles from Edinburgh airport, and then appears to fall asleep in the conference chamber – surely the most carbon-intensive afternoon nap in history. Russian President Vladimir Putin and Chinese President Xi Jinping haven't bothered to come at all – the latter an especial disappointment given that his country accounts for 33 percent of the world's carbon emissions.[4] As for Putin, he recorded a video message for the forestry and land use conference part of COP26, but that was all.

A few promises and pledges are wrung out of world leaders. Xi Jinping has already said that his country will try to become carbon neutral by 2060, a full decade after the UN would like – and, unlike Britain's commitment to reach net zero, it isn't written into law. India's Prime Minister Narendra Modi says his country will attempt to eliminate net carbon emissions by ten years later, in 2070 – but he wants huge sums of Western money in return for his pledges. A deal is cobbled together in the hope of decreasing the rate of deforestation in some countries – although within two days Indonesia has already begun to pour cold water on the deal by saying that it will not allow the deforestation deal to get in the way of development; in other words it will continue to chop down trees where that is required to create new oil palm plantations and the like. Seventy-seven countries sign a pledge to phase out coal power by 2030 (in the case of developed countries) or by 2040 (in the case of developing ones). But even then many countries only sign because of the caveat 'or as soon as possible thereafter'. Joe Biden – worshipped by progressives who see him as the antithesis of the isolationist Donald Trump – is expected to be among those who sign. Then, a day beforehand, his Democratic party loses the governorship of the state of Virginia – which has a big coal-mining industry – and Biden wobbles, declining to sign.

The final pact commits no country to do anything by any particular date. It is a mish-mash concocted to offer something to everyone. It takes care to include, for example, the phrase 'climate justice', which has been wafted around on placards outside the hall by activists. Yet the pact places no legal commitment on any countries to phase out the burning of fossil fuels (although Britain and a few other countries have placed that commitment on themselves). India and China successfully object to a clause which mentions 'accelerating efforts to phase out unabated coal power', so that the words 'phase out' are replaced with 'phase down' – whatever that means. As India points out, the communiqué says nothing about phasing out oil and gas, so why should countries with coal reserves suffer? Britain and other wealthy nations, on the other hand, agree to a clause regretting that they haven't yet stumped up the £100 billion of cash they have promised to pay poorer countries to help them cope with a transition away from fossil fuel, and demanding that they double this promised sum. That, and the reference to 'climate justice', makes it clear what is coming: there are going to be multiple demands for cash from any country which fancies it – and it is going to come out of the pockets of taxpayers in wealthy countries. Any country with high historical carbon emissions – and Britain, as the seat of the industrial revolution, is top of the list – is going to be on the hook.

Where does this fit with climate science? That concentrations of carbon dioxide in the atmosphere have increased since the mass burning of fossil fuels is beyond doubt. So, too, is the warming trend in global temperatures over the past century and a half – which, according to the Intergovernmental Panel on Climate Change (IPCC), has seen global temperatures rise by an average of between 0.8 and 1.3 degrees Celsius. How much of the latter is caused by the former is something we can never know for sure, but the conclusion of the IPCC that 'it is unequivocal that human influence has warmed the atmosphere, ocean and land' is not unreasonable. That it would be better if we weren't changing the composition of the atmosphere is something on which we ought all be able to agree. The world has a strong incentive to reduce, even eventually eliminate, emissions of carbon dioxide and other greenhouse gas emissions.

Yet the political campaign for net zero has gone way beyond what climate science can stand. It has become a world where every climatic extreme, every piece of adverse weather, is blamed on human influence and is a portent of an even more doom-laden future to come. Hence a heatwave in July 2022, which set a new high-temperature record in Britain and sparked wildfires in the Gironde department of south-western France, becomes a 'heat apocalypse' in the words of a French meteorologist.[5] A Norfolk garden which suffered a fire in the heat became a scene 'like Armageddon'.[6] We are told by an 8-year-old climate activist that 'the planet is dying',[7] that 320 million people face starvation by 2030.[8]

The constant use of such language and assertion helps us neither understand climate change nor come up with a reasoned policy on what to do about it. It is just silly, emotional language, with news organisations, politicians, state officials and campaigners trying to outdo each other in the extremeness of their language. We hear constantly, too, of how climate change is supposedly causing devastating floods, storms, tornados and even freezing spells. In contrast to rising temperatures, for which we have good data, the claim that climate change is bringing us other kinds of extreme and undesirable weather is somewhat less supported by data. On the contrary, as we shall see later on, in some cases data points in the opposite direction to the lazy claims being made.

There are two wings to the net zero movement. The first argues that the only route to salvation is for us all to reduce our living standards, to abandon consumerism or even to do away with capitalism for good. This is the wing represented at its extreme end by Extinction Rebellion and other protest groups. The second argues that technology will save us without us having to make great sacrifices – indeed, it often asserts that far from costing us, the net zero target will end up enriching us by unleashing a rush of wealth-creating innovation that otherwise would not have taken place. The market, somehow, will provide. This is broadly the position of Britain's Conservative government.

Both these wings have lost touch with reality. The first, because it overstates climate science and because it fails to grasp that people – the poor especially – are not going to accept being made poorer. Going vegan, or giving up the car commute for a morning cycle ride might be pleasant-enough options for the well-off, but the poor are not going to be prepared to shiver or go hungry in the name of cutting carbon emissions. And they really would shiver and go hungry. If you want to reach net zero over the next few years through the curtailment of lifestyles you are not going to achieve it without returning society to a pre-industrial level of subsistence.

But the second school of thought is equally naive in expecting technology magically to allow us to achieve net zero emissions without any reduction in our living standards. The industrial revolution of the 18th century, and all subsequent advances which have transformed human societies, have been based on one thing above all others: a source of cheap, concentrated energy – whether that be coal, oil or nuclear. To expect the same level of wealth in an economy based on far less dense forms of energy, such as wind and solar – which appears to be the current expectation of the UK government and other European governments – is not realistic. To expect to be able to achieve net zero without a serious cost to the economy is no more than Panglossian optimism. It would require multiple forms of new technology which either have not yet been invented or which have yet to be proven on a commercial scale. And it would require all this to be achieved in less than 30 years' time.

Whenever you make these points, however, they tend to be batted away with the generalised assertion – without any evidence to support it – that 'the costs of acting are much less than the costs of not acting' (if, indeed, you are not dismissed as a 'denier'). The prospects of future climate change are so grim, we are told, that failing to commit to net zero by 2050, or some date very soon after that, is simply not an option.

Really? Throughout COP26 we keep hearing about 'the science' – a supposed set of truths which cannot be challenged. But it is remarkable how few actual climate scientists are delivering the lectures at COP26; those who undertook the painstaking studies which went into the IPCC report published three months earlier, and whose work points to some interesting, some conflicting changes in the climate but hardly to cataclysm, seem mysteriously absent. Climate change is a world that has come to be controlled by activists and campaigners who claim to be on the side of science and reason but who are really spinning narratives which suit ulterior motives.

By the end of COP26 it becomes painfully clear that there is a schism between mostly European countries, which, in keeping with the fiery rhetoric of many from the podium, have resolved to eliminate their carbon emissions at any cost, and those like Russia, China and the United States, which have signalled very clearly that while they will try to reduce emissions they will not compromise economic growth in order to do so. While plenty have made promises and expressed aspirations, Britain remains one of the very few countries to have tied itself down with a legally binding commitment to reach net zero emissions by 2050.

Glasgow is the confirmation of a political alignment which has been in the making for several years but which now becomes visible with even more clarity. It is no longer West versus East, North versus South, but the committed players in the fight against climate change and the less committed players. They are playing a very, very different game, with very different consequences for their citizens.

2.

Self-sacrifice

IN MAY 2019 THERESA MAY, the Prime Minister of the United Kingdom, was on her way out, her short and unhappy time in office nearly at an end. Her three-year premiership had been dominated by Brexit – Britain's departure from the European Union – for which the British public had, shockingly to some, voted in 2016. Some blamed May for failing to secure a trade deal, or even a withdrawal deal, with the EU. Others saw her as the victim of her own MPs, who had been unable to agree on any of the possible deals that she had put before the House of Commons. By now her position was untenable, and a leadership election to choose a successor as Conservative Party leader and Prime Minister was underway.

On her way out of the door, however, she planted a very large bomb to be detonated beneath her successors. Amid the drama and chaos of Brexit, it was hardly even noticed by the British public. Yet it had far greater implications – and potentially far more destructive power – than even the matter of Britain's departure from the EU. The bomb had the seemingly innocuous name 'Climate Change Act (2050 Target Amendment) Order 2019'. It wasn't even a new Parliamentary act, rather a small amendment to one which had been passed eleven years earlier, the Climate Change Act 2008. Whereas the original act had legally committed Britain to reduce greenhouse gas emissions by 80 percent (relative to 1990 levels) by 2050, the new amendment demanded that net emissions be reduced to net zero by this date – with any lingering emissions compensated for by measures to remove carbon dioxide and other greenhouse gases from the atmosphere.

The change was nodded through by the House of Commons without even a vote. In the hour and a half allotted for debate only one MP expressed reservations – Labour backbencher Graham Stringer, one of the few members of the House of Commons with scientific qualifications, asked why the government had not produced an 'impact assessment' as it does with most pieces of legislation and was told by a government minister that it wasn't necessary. Two days later the House of Lords – the upper house of the UK Parliament – did hold a vote and passed an amendment complaining that the government had 'given little detail of how the emissions target will be met' and that it had 'made a substantial change in policy without the full and proper scrutiny that such a change deserves'. But the Lords didn't actually oppose the net zero target – they voted for it in spite of complaining the government had failed to show any indication as to how it could be reached. And thus, with hardly a whimper, a piece of legislation with huge implications for UK citizens and UK industries became law.

Net zero. It sounded a noble objective. As Chris Skidmore, the government minister who introduced the bill to the House of Commons, observed, it would mean Britain becoming the first major economy in the world to make a legally binding commitment to eliminate greenhouse emissions. But what did it really mean, what was it going to cost, and did any of the MPs who had just nodded it through actually understand the implications?

The government's case was based around a claim made some months earlier by the Climate Change Committee (CCC) – which advises the government on climate policy – that achieving net zero emissions by 2050 would cost between 1 and 2 percent of GDP per annum by 2050 – roughly equating to an eventual bill of £1 trillion by that date. But this, said the minister, was before you took into account the many benefits, such as increased air quality and what he called 'green-collar jobs'. Moreover, he implied that falling costs would reduce the bill further. Forget the bill, in other words; it will be a modest fee given what we will gain.

Not one MP pointed out the folly: how can you possibly estimate the cost of doing something when you have no idea how it can be done? By 2019, Britain was well on its way to phasing out coal power and generating around 15 percent of its electricity from wind farms and solar farms. A small proportion of electric cars were already on the road. But fossil fuel-free aviation? Decarbonisation of the steel and cement industries? Satisfying an enormous hike in demand for power as cars and domestic heating were switched from oil and gas to electricity? Energy storage to cope with the intermittent nature of wind and solar energy? These were among the many technological problems with which the country had hardly begun to grapple. While in some cases solutions might exist in theory or have been demonstrated on a laboratory-scale, no one knew whether they could successfully be scaled up and at what cost. As John Kerry, the US climate envoy, was later to say, half the technology which will be required to achieve net zero has yet to be invented.[1] The UK Parliament, however, had just approved a law obligating the country to net zero with no idea of how, when or whether that technology would be developed – and not the faintest idea of what it would really cost.

When National Grid ESO – the company which runs the electricity grid in Britain – attempted to calculate its own estimate of the cost of reaching net zero by 2050 it came up with an answer dramatically different to that of the CCC. In 2020 it presented four different scenarios of how Britain might attempt the transition, involving different blends of renewable energy, changes in consumer behaviour and so on. Its estimated costings in each case came out at around £160 billion a year of investment, eventually reaching a total of around £3 trillion.[2] That was three times the figure which the CCC had touted just a year earlier – and National Grid was only trying to price up the decarbonisation of the energy sector, not agriculture and difficult-to-decarbonise sectors such as steel and cement. To MPs who had treated the CCC's figure as gospel, and nodded through the 2050 target, it was a sharp reminder that they had committed the country to an open-ended bill, the eventual size of which no one could reasonably guess – other than to say it was going to be huge. Those MPs knew full well the government's lousy record on estimating costs of things we do know how to do – such as building a high-speed railway in the shape of HS2 from London to Birmingham, Manchester and Leeds, whose estimated costs nearly trebled from £37.5 billion in 2009 to £107 billion in 2019.[3] Yet they had swallowed whole an attempt to put a price on doing something which had vastly more unknowns and which involved technologies yet to be invented or proved on a commercial scale.

It took two years for the government itself to come up with some kind of plan of how it would reach net zero. Britain could do it 'without so much as a hair shirt in sight', wrote Prime Minister Boris Johnson in the foreword to his Net Zero Strategy, published in October 2021. 'No one will be required to rip out their existing boiler or scrap their current car.' By 2035, the document went on to say, the UK would be powered entirely by clean electricity 'subject to security of supply'. To this end it was going to invest in floating wind farms and, by 2024, make a decision as to how to fund a large nuclear plant (yes, just one, and it was only the decision that would be made by 2024; it would take another decade or so to build). There would be investment in hydrogen, so that hopefully by 2035 we might have a public hydrogen supply to replace the gas supply (although a decision on whether to pursue this was delayed until 2026). Also by 2035, the price of electric heat pumps might have come down – *might* – to make them a practical replacement for new gas boilers which would by then be banned. New petrol and diesel cars would be banned from 2030, hybrids from 2035. There would be £750 million of investment to plant new woodlands and restore peat bogs.

But the Net Zero Strategy left more questions unanswered than it answered. How are we to establish security of electricity supply if we come to rely even more on intermittent renewables? How is one nuclear power station going to solve our problems when it – along with the one currently under construction at Hinkley in Somerset – won't even replace Britain's seven existing nuclear power stations, all of which are due to reach the end of their working lives by 2035? Does the government really have confidence that it will turn out to be economical to produce hydrogen by zero-carbon means – as opposed to manufacturing it from coal and gas, as almost all the world's hydrogen is currently produced? You can order us all to buy electric cars, but how are you going to make sure that the cars are themselves zero carbon, given that a hefty proportion of a vehicle's lifetime's emissions are tied up in its manufacture? If we are going to cover the countryside with woodland, where does that leave food production? Are we going to be even more reliant on importing it from overseas, with the consequence that our food might end up with a higher carbon footprint than now?

On top of that was left dangling the biggest question of all: what is it all going to cost us, and who is going to end up paying the bill? On the same day that the Net Zero Strategy was published, the Treasury produced its own assessment of the costs of net zero. Did the Treasury agree with the Climate Change Committee's assessment that it would cost no more than £1 trillion, or National Grid's estimate of £3 trillion for the energy sector alone? It couldn't say. It offered no estimate of the cost of net zero, arguing, rather, that it wasn't possible to make such an estimate at this stage. As for who will pay, that was at least becoming clear. We were all going to be paying, either through our taxes or through supplements on our energy bills.

Britain, in short, is to embark on an experiment unique in human history, in which it voluntarily rejects whole areas of established technology which currently make society and the economy function, and tries to replace them with novel technologies, some of which do not currently exist and others of which may exist on a demonstration level but have not yet been scaled up. And the whole project has to be completed in just 27 years, no allowances, no wriggle room. It will be an industrial revolution to put all previous periods of human progress in the shade – if it can be achieved. But there is a very, very big and expensive 'if' there. It is generally good to be ambitious and optimistic. There is a point, however, at which it becomes foolishness.

Is there even a Plan B in case technology disappoints and it proves not possible to decarbonise Britain without causing huge damage to the economy? I asked the business secretary, Kwasi Kwarteng, this in October 2021 and he denied there was a need for such a plan. No minister seems brave enough to say that the 2050 target may have to be revisited. Asked in July 2022 whether they were committed to the 2050 target, all five remaining Conservative leadership candidates confirmed that they were – although one, Kemi Badenoch, had previously suggested the target might have to be moved out to 2060 or 2070.[4] All objection to the Net Zero Strategy has been brushed aside by government ministers who insist there really is no alternative: so dire is the climate emergency that we simply have to decarbonise everything we do – fail to do so and we will be lashed by ever more dramatic weather: tossed, boiled, frozen and drowned. Behind it, though, lies a Little Englander fantasy: that somehow we can tackle climate change on our own, even if other countries do not follow our example. Yet Britain accounts for less than 1 percent of global emissions (or a bit more if you count them on a consumption basis rather than emissions basis, as we shall see later).

Meanwhile, on the other side of the world, China, which accounts for 33 percent of global emissions, is addressing climate change in its own way – one which isn't going to put constraints on its industries or involve the impoverishment of its people. And many other countries are adopting the same attitude.

3.

Meanwhile, in China

THE COP26 CONFERENCE WAS PRECEDED by a number of incidents of adverse weather over the summer of 2021 which increasingly came to be blamed on man-made climate change. A heatwave in British Columbia, floods in the Rhineland, wildfires in California and Turkey; all were depicted as signs of a growing climate emergency which was taking even climate scientists by surprise with its ferocity.

Or at least they were in the West. World Weather Attribution, a joint project by Imperial College London, the Royal Netherlands Meteorological Institute, the Red Cross Red Crescent Climate Centre and others, published a study which at first sight appeared to blame the Rhineland floods fairly and squarely on man-made climate change. Rainfall of the intensity which had occurred on the two days before the Rhineland floods, media reports confidently stated, was now up to nine times as likely to occur as it was in the mid-19th century, when the world was 1.2 degrees Celsius cooler than it is now. Anyone who bothered to read the paper itself would have reached a somewhat different conclusion. The modelling used in the study had produced such a wide spread of results – it suggested that the risk of such rainfall had increased by between 1.2 and 9 times – as to be meaningless. The scientists indeed admitted that their analysis 'pushes the limits of what current methods of extreme event attribution are designed for'.[1] Moreover, the study only assessed the risk of the rainfall experienced on the two days immediately prior to the floods. Yet, as was admitted, a large factor behind the floods was the state of the ground prior to those two days – it was saturated after weeks of above-average rain. In fact, climate models have tended to predict drier summers for the Rhineland,[2] suggesting that the peculiar set of circumstances which preceded the floods of July 2021 might be less likely to occur in a warmer world.

This did not stop the summer's floods from becoming a rallying cry for COP26, with Alok Sharma, the president of the event, describing flooding in the UK as a 'sober reminder' of why the world desperately needed to cut carbon emissions. Surveying the damage in the Rhineland, German Chancellor Angela Merkel said: 'We have to hurry, we have to get faster in the fight against climate change.'

In China, however, a very different attitude prevailed. The week following the Rhineland floods saw serious floods in the Henan province of central China. In the city of Zhengzhou, several passengers were drowned on metro trains. Across the region as a whole, 302 people were reported to have died.[3] Coming hot on the heels of the German floods, Western media were quick to attribute the disaster to climate change. It was widely reported to have been the heaviest rain in a thousand years – a claim which seems to have emanated from the meteorological station at Zhengzhou but which stands at odds with the meteorological record. Although there is some evidence that heavy precipitation is increasing in China, the deluge of 2021 was far from unprecedented; worse had occurred in living memory. In July 2021 Zhengzhou recorded 24 inches of rain over three days. Yet at Linzhuang, close to the Banqiao Dam 100 miles to the south, 1,605 mm of rain (63 inches) was recorded over the same period in 1975 when Typhoon Nina struck; 830 mm (33 inches) fell in a single six-hour period. On that occasion, 26,000 people were killed directly by the flood, 10 million people were left homeless

and a further 100,000 deaths were attributed to the famine
and disease which followed.[4]

In contrast to Western media, in China there was little
attempt to blame the 2021 deluge on climate change. Ren
Guoyu of China's National Climate Centre was reported to
have 'dismissed the connection between heavy rain in
Zhengzhou and global climate change' and instead blamed it
on 'abnormal planetary scale atmospheric circulation' –
weather, in other words.[5]

Climate change has not gone unrecognised by the Chinese
government. For the past decade the China Meteorological
Administration Association has published a 'Blue Book' giving
its own assessment of climate change, which closely matches
that of the IPCC (the IPCC report itself that is, not the reporting
of it). The 2020 edition, for example, declares that average global
temperatures have risen by 1.1 degrees Celsius 'since preindus-
trial times'. As far as rainfall is concerned, it notes that 'heavy
precipitation events' increased in China between 1961 and 2019.[6]

Nor is China absent from efforts to decarbonise its economy.
While continuing to build new coal plants the country is a
heavy investor in renewable energy. Indeed, it is the world
leader. In 2021, according to the International Renewable
Energy Agency, it had 282 GW of installed capacity of wind
power, along with 254 GW of solar. The next country on the
list, the United States, had 118 GW of wind power and 76
GW of solar.[7]

In September 2020, addressing the UN via video, Chinese
President Xi Jinping had a surprising announcement to
make. Having previously avoided committing his country
to reach net zero carbon emissions, he was now suggesting
that China would reach this goal by 2060: 'Guided by the
vision of building a community with a shared future for
mankind, China will continue to make extraordinary efforts
to scale up its nationally determined contributions. China

will adopt even more forceful policies and measures, and strive to peak carbon dioxide emissions before 2030 and achieve carbon neutrality before 2060, thus making greater efforts and contributions toward meeting the objectives of the Paris Agreement.'

Did he really mean it, or was it a political ploy, an attempt to boost the image of China in the eyes of European countries angry with Donald Trump for pulling out of the Paris Agreement, the 2015 treaty which supposedly committed signatories to produce a strategy consistent with maintaining global temperatures at no more than 1.5 degrees Celsius above pre-industrial levels? What Xi Jinping announced certainly wasn't a legally binding promise in the way that Britain, France and a few other countries have committed themselves to reach net zero by 2050. It was merely an aspiration. China had often attracted criticism in the West for its enthusiasm for building coal-fired power stations. Xi Jinping's 2060 announcement batted away such criticism, putting China into the company of the righteous – while simultaneously confirming that the world's largest economy and world's biggest polluter still intends to increase its carbon emissions for the next decade at least.

In the run-up to COP26, the Chinese government's mixed messages began to confuse Western observers. In September 2021 Xi Jinping announced, in a recorded speech to the UN General Assembly, that China would no longer finance new coal-fired power stations overseas, in countries such as Indonesia and Bangladesh where it had been active in the industry. The speech was hailed by US climate envoy John Kerry as a 'great contribution', while Alok Sharma announced that the 'writing is on the wall for coal'.

Not so fast. A week later, global coal and gas prices spiked as the global economy continued to recover from the Covid-19 pandemic. China, especially, was caught in an energy crunch. The government was forced to order factories to suspend production, with some homes, too, being put into blackout. Emergency coal mines were reopened to feed demand, and Xi Jinping issued an order for state energy companies to outbid other global customers for what gas and oil was available on international markets – so as to ensure the lights could be kept on through the winter. Following a meeting of China's National Energy Commission, Prime Minister Li Keqiang suggested that China's targets for achieving net zero emissions might be revised – perhaps stretched out over a longer period. Energy security, he asserted, would be the priority. Dirtier coal-fired power plants would be closed, but cleaner ones would be opened where appropriate. The coal age, it seemed, was not quite so dead after all. The writing had been scrubbed off the wall.

What to make of all this? Does China care about climate change or not? There is a very clear answer, if you follow the government's pronouncements: yes, China does want to be part of an international effort to tackle climate change through a transition to cleaner energy. But no, it is not going to sacrifice economic growth in order to get to net zero by any specific date – however much Western leaders might want to push for that.

China's intentions on decarbonisation were made reasonably clear with the publication of the *14th Five-Year Plan* in March 2021. The document repeats the aspiration made in Xi Jinping's speech, but again stops well short of a legally binding commitment: 'We will focus our efforts on achieving carbon neutrality by 2060 and adopt more forceful policies and measures.' It does make a couple of binding commitments on carbon emissions, but not ones which necessarily mean that emissions will fall any time soon. It declares that in the forthcoming half decade 'energy consumption and carbon dioxide emissions per unit of GDP will be reduced by 13.5 percent and 18 percent respectively'.[8]

The important words here are 'per unit of GDP'. It amounts to a commitment to improve energy efficiency, but allows for emissions to grow with the economy. Given that the Chinese economy has typically grown at between 6 and 7 percent in recent years, and so GDP can be expected to grow by between 35 and 40 percent over the course of the five-year plan, it doesn't really amount to a commitment to reduce carbon emissions by a single puff.

The five-year plan contains plenty of talk of investment in green energy, eagerly picked up by environmentalists in the West:

> We will accelerate the development of non-fossil energy, adhere to both centralised and distributed methods simultaneously, vigorously increase the scale of wind power and photovoltaic power generation . . . orderly develop offshore wind power, accelerate the construction of the Southwest Hydropower Base, safely and steadily promote the construction of coastal nuclear power . . . and increase the proportion of non-fossil energy in total energy consumption to about 20 percent.

But it certainly isn't intended to be the end of fossil fuel investment. On the contrary, the plan goes on:

> We will promote the concentration of coal production in resource-rich areas, reasonably control the scale and development pace of coal power construction, and promote the replacement of coal with electricity. We will liberalise market access for oil and gas exploration and development in an orderly manner, accelerate the utilisation of deep-sea, deep-seated and unconventional oil and gas resources, and promote an increase in oil and gas reserves and production.

In other words, coal-mining, fracking, oil, gas, all the things which raise hackles in Britain, attracting lawsuits from environmentalists who claim they are inconsistent with the legally binding target of reaching net zero emissions by 2050: China is committed to expanding them all. China has set itself on an intended path towards net zero emissions, but it is a path which very much winds through the coal fields and oil wells.

In contrast to the reaction of many UK commentators to the floods of 2021, China's five-year plan does not see cutting carbon emissions as a means of averting some kind of imminent meteorological emergency. On the contrary, it treats floods as largely random weather events requiring ongoing investment in flood defences. There is one mention of adapting infrastructure to climate change, but the section on flood defences does not even mention the climate, which would be sure to dominate such a document in the West:

> We will implement flood control upgrading projects, address the weak links in flood control, accelerate the construction of flood control hub projects, the management of small- and medium-size rivers, and the reinforcement of dangerous reservoirs, and comprehensively promote the construction of dikes and flood storage and detention areas. We will strengthen the protection and restoration of water conservation areas, increase the protection and comprehensive governance strength for key rivers and lakes, and restore the aquatic ecosystem to provide clear waters and green banks.

Put all this together and China's policy on decarbonising its economy is pretty clear: yes, we want to eliminate carbon emissions when we can, but it is not going to happen at the expense of the economy or the living standards of our people. We will clean up our industry because we think climate change is a problem, but no, we don't think it is an existential threat to human civilisation. At all times we will put energy security ahead of decarbonisation. This was further confirmed in a speech by Xi Jinping in January 2022, after a winter of high fuel prices, in which he said that cutting carbon emissions was not going to come at the expense of energy and food security or the 'normal life' of the country's citizens. In other words, there was going to be no telling the people that life-styles will have to change.[9]

This is set against a policy followed by Britain, and some other European countries, which can be summed up as follows: we are so terrified of climate change that we have unilaterally committed ourselves to eliminate all net carbon emissions within the next three decades, at whatever cost – and whether other countries follow or not. We don't yet know how we are going to do that without returning our people to pre-industrial poverty, but hopefully something will turn up.

There are serious implications here: while Britain has set about solving climate change in an atmosphere of panic and end-of-times rhetoric, China's preoccupation lies with becoming the world's chief economic superpower. That many Western countries are prepared to hinder their economies by tying them down to become net zero by 2050, or in some cases before, can only help China. China might be a dicta-torship, a violator of human rights, a country with a poor environmental record, a land in which few Westerners might choose to live; but on the matter of climate change it may come to be envied in the West. It has adopted a policy which has been calculated to advance its interests, not one of self-sacrifice.

4.

And Russia . . .

As with China, Russia hasn't entirely ignored international pressure to act on carbon emissions. Vladimir Putin has supposedly committed himself to trying to reach net zero carbon emissions by 2060 – putting him in the company of the majority of the world's nations in trying to address climate change. But in February 2022 we found just how committed Putin is to culturing relations with the world at large. Having lined up his tanks on the Ukrainian border and spent weeks denying that he was planning an invasion, on the morning of 24 February the tanks rolled in anyway – exactly on cue with predictions by Western intelligence agencies. As the bombs and shells began to take out airfields and blasted at apartment blocks, the task of cutting carbon emissions seemed a very long way from Russia's priorities. Putin was certainly not using plug-in electric tanks nor hydrogen-powered missile-launchers. The only hydrogen-powered military equipment that the Russian leader did raise the spectre of using was hydrogen bombs: he put his country on nuclear alert.

The dramatic events reminded everyone that, while climate change is of course an important issue, it is folly to try to claim that it is the most serious threat facing the world. The gravest threat to civilisation now, as at every point during the past 70 years, is a rogue state with nuclear weapons. And in Vladimir Putin's Russia, we now have that deadly combination.

The West replied rapidly to the Russian invasion of Ukraine

with sanctions. Russian banks were frozen out of the Brussels-based SWIFT system for settling international financial transactions. Western companies withdrew from Russian-based investments. A few oligarchs had bank accounts frozen. Russian sports teams were banned from competing in international competitions. The sanctions had some effect: the rouble, never the strongest of currencies, plummeted – although it had more than recovered those losses by June. Russian interest rates were jacked up to over 20 percent. Queues formed outside food shops, reminiscent of Soviet days.

Yet Western Europe was hamstrung over what economic action it could take against Putin's regime, for the simple reason that, at the time of the invasion, 40 percent of European gas was supplied from Russia. While Germany and other European countries announced that they would try to wean themselves off Russian oil and gas – in Germany's case all but eliminating Russian gas imports by the middle of 2024 – it was Putin who took the initiative by cutting the amount of gas flowing through the Nord Stream 1 pipeline. By the end of July 2022 it was already down to 20 percent of what it had been before the invasion. The EU was forced to put together a hurried deal in which member states agreed to slash gas consumption by 15 percent – by closing factories or rationing gas supplies to homes – to avert a disorderly collapse in the supply network.

Just how did Europe allow itself to become so dependent on Russia for energy, when it is itself rich in natural gas? For years, energy policy across Europe had become driven by environmental concerns while ignoring geopolitical ones. While countries ran down their own oil and gas industries in an effort to meet their net zero commitments, they continued to see Russian oil and gas as a useful stopgap. In Germany's case, the government pandered to the anti-nuclear lobby by closing three of the country's remaining six nuclear power stations at New Year 2022, even when Putin's tanks were already lined up on the Ukraine border. In this case, the move not only increased reliance on Russian gas, it also eliminated a low-carbon source of energy.

As for Putin, like Xi Jinping, he was happy to pander to Western demands for a net zero strategy of his own. But did it amount to anything in reality? Let's have a look.

Although Vladimir Putin didn't bother himself to turn up to COP26 in Glasgow, and tried to play down its importance, his government did publish its Low Carbon Development Strategy on the eve of the conference. If you were looking to see a positive side to Putin's regime this document made the right sort of noises, even employing fashionable buzz-phrases like the 'circular economy'. The strategy presents two scenarios for Russia: a 'business as usual' scenario which sees greenhouse gas emissions rise by 8 percent by 2030 and 25 percent by 2050 – but where energy exports fall by 2.8 percent a year as a result of the rest of Europe switching to clean energy. Instead, it proposes an 'intensive' scenario with the aim of 'ensuring global competitiveness and sustainable economic growth of the Russian Federation'. Under this scenario, greenhouse emissions would fall by 60 percent on 2019 levels by 2050 (or 80 percent on 1990 levels), and be eliminated by 2060.

But as with China, there is absolutely nothing in Russia's approach that puts the country under any legal obligation to reach net zero by 2060 or any other date. Moreover, even the 'intensive' scenario foresees emissions rising until 2030 – and it allows plenty of room for gas and coal. 'The potential for reducing greenhouse gas emissions in coal-fired power generation is used to the maximum,' it states, 'including through a complete transition to the best-available technology, support for innovative and climate-efficient technology for burning coal, widespread replacement of low-efficiency boiler houses with cogeneration facilities, the widespread promotion and use of carbon capture and storage.'[1] So, there is no intention to phase out coal power. As for gas, the plan proposes to switch to combined-cycle gas power plants (as opposed to less efficient open-cycle plants) – which have been standard in Britain for decades.

So what is at the heart of the Russian plan to reach net zero emissions? 'It is planned to increase the area of managed forests, and we will look into studying and assessing the potential for increasing the absorption of greenhouse gases by forests.' It goes on to say that it hopes to achieve this by replacing pine forests with mixed woodland and to improve firefighting so as to reduce the amount of forest burned annually. In other words, Russia intends to use its vast land area to try to absorb carbon dioxide and so counter rather than eliminate emissions from power generation and industrial processes. That is relatively easy to do, it has to be said, when your country has such an expanse of forests as Russia does.

Of all countries, Russia ought to be in the best position to achieve net zero carbon emissions. With a low population density and many very long, wide and strong-flowing rivers, it possesses huge hydro-electric potential. It has vast reserves of timber for construction. As far as you can mop up residual carbon emissions by planting trees, Russia has huge steppe lands for doing this – indeed, with higher temperatures pushing the tree line northwards, you don't even have to take the trouble to plant them in order to claim that your forests are sequestrating large, extra quantities of carbon dioxide. Yet it is not Russia which has legally committed itself to eliminating net carbon emissions; it is Britain, in spite of being in a much worse position to do so.

The Russian Low Carbon Development Plan, like much else to come out of Putin's Russia, is not something to be trusted. In order to continue to do business with the EU,

Russia was effectively obliged to come up with some kind of pledge to reach net zero carbon emissions at some point in the future. But in doing so, Russia ensured that, in the short term at least, it was able to build European dependence on Russian gas. While Western European countries have been running down their fossil fuel industries, declining to develop new fields in the North Sea, passing up the chance to exploit recently discovered reserves of shale gas, Russia has continued to ramp up gas production and build new pipelines to Western Europe in order to export it. In 2019 alone, European gas production (excluding Russia) fell by 6 percent, thanks in part to the Dutch government capping production from its North Sea fields in order to meet climate obligations. European gas production (excluding Norway) is forecast by the International Energy Agency to fall by a further 40 percent by 2025.[2] Russia, by contrast, increased overall production by 1.7 percent in 2019. But it wasn't that Europe was consuming less gas – on the contrary, gas power plants increased their output by 11 percent as the continent switched away from dirtier coal plants.[3] To put it bluntly, Europe was trying to wash away its climate sins by curtailing its own gas production while consuming increased quantities of the stuff imported from elsewhere.

Geopolitical considerations simply hadn't entered into the formulation of European energy policy. All that mattered was cutting Europe's carbon emissions in order to reach the 2050 net zero target (or 2045 in the case of Germany). This was in spite of the obvious: that it is pointless pursuing this target if other large emitters are not going to play ball. The price was to weaken Europe politically and to put itself at the mercy of Vladimir Putin's expansionist ambitions. In spite of trying to boycott Russia, in the first 100 days after the invasion of Ukraine, EU states imported €57 billion worth of fossil fuels from the country.[4]

Britain's – and Europe's – dependence on Russian fossil fuels could so easily have been avoided. Until 2003, thanks to the North Sea, Britain was self-sufficient in energy. But by 2013 the country was importing half of its energy requirements. Much of this was down to the inevitable running down and exhaustion of prime oil and gas fields in the North Sea, yet in recent years the government has discouraged further investment in new fields. Meanwhile, successive governments have blown hot and cold on the exploitation of an alternative source of energy: shale gas. For many years, policy was to forget UK gas and invest in renewables instead – making up the gap in the short term by importing liquefied natural gas (LNG). However, dependence on imported gas has amplified a global crunch in gas supply – by April 2022 domestic bills had risen by more than 50 percent on a year earlier. In 2020, 60 percent of the 811 TWh of gas consumed in Britain was imported. Just over half came via pipelines from Norway and the Netherlands and the rest in refrigerated ships from the United States, Qatar and Russia.[5]

Yet, even now, Britain could still be self-sufficient in gas – had its embryonic shale gas industry been allowed to develop. There are widely varying estimates of how much gas lies beneath Britain, and how much of it could potentially be extracted and used, but even if you take the lowest estimate quoted by the British Geological Survey – 140 trillion cubic feet – that would be enough to feed current demand for gas for 47 years.[6] It is over a decade since commercial firms started trial drilling and still, not a single puff of UK-produced shale gas has yet made it into British homes. Drilling and hydraulic fracturing – or 'fracking' – near Blackpool was suspended after a number of minor earth tremors and then in 2019 the government placed a moratorium on drilling. In Scotland fracking has been banned altogether. This is all in spite of

fracking being a tried and tested technology in the United
States. A 2012 report by the Royal Society and Royal Academy
of Engineering concluded that fracking could safely be carried
out in Britain so long as suitable precautions were taken.[7]
Fracking is not without environmental issues – as with any
oil or gas production, badly sealed boreholes can potentially
pollute water-bearing rock, and it can cause minor earth
tremors. However, lurid claims made in the 2010 film *Gasland*
that fracking had allowed methane to seep into drinking water
to the extent that residents could set alight gas emanating
from their taps have long since been debunked.[8] As the Royal
Society and Royal Academy of Engineering explained in its
review of fracking safety in 2012, in no case in the United
States has drinking water been found to be contaminated by
the tell-tale chemicals used in the fracking process. In many
cases, naturally occurring methane was known to have been
present in drinking water long before hydraulic fracturing
began.[9]

So, instead of exploiting its own shale gas, Britain imports
shale gas from the United States. Forgoing the country's own
reserves has not cut carbon emissions. Quite the opposite – it
generates more emissions because the gas has to be compressed
into liquid form and refrigerated before being shipped across
the Atlantic. Indeed, the liquefaction, transport and regasification process can itself consume up to 10 percent of the gas
being transported.[10]

Domestic production of gas – which per unit of energy
emits only half as much carbon dioxide as does coal – should
have been encouraged as the transition fuel between coal and
clean energy. Gas power plants are, at present, by far the most
reliable and affordable means by which we can make up for
the gaps in generation from wind and solar plants. They can
be fired up at short notice, are much more responsive to
changes in demand than nuclear plants and are vastly cheaper

than energy storage. Yet Britain has instead chosen to wind down its gas industry.

Moreover, in Russia's case, the energy policies being pursued by Britain and the rest of Western Europe have helped reduce our ability to respond to military aggression. Vladimir Putin, whose own carbon reduction plans stop well short of any measures which would damage his own economy, must be laughing at our naivety.

5.

An example not being followed

IF BRITAIN WERE TO SUCCEED in achieving net zero emissions it would not be able to boast of being the first country to get there. Suriname and Bhutan are estimated by the Energy & Climate Intelligence Unit to have reached that status already (thanks to being heavily wooded) – although, given that they stand at 99th and 127th respectively in the UN's Human Development Index, few would envy their achievement. But Britain can already boast – if that is the appropriate word – of being one of the few countries which has legally committed itself to reducing net greenhouse gas emissions by a prescribed date. Many have set aspirations to do so, but that is a very different matter from setting the target into law – and thus inviting people and organisations to sue the government if it fails to deliver.

It is not straightforward to come up with a list of countries which have committed themselves legally to net zero emissions, as legal language varies from country to country and it is not always clear whether a failure to reach net zero could be actioned or not. But the Energy & Climate Intelligence Unit produced the following list in 2022:

> Germany (must be net zero by 2045)
> Sweden (2045)
> Japan (2050)
> UK (2050)
> France (2050)

Canada (2050)
South Korea (2050)
Spain (2050)
Ireland (2050)
Chile (2050)
Portugal (2050)
Denmark (2050)
New Zealand (2050)
Hungary (2050)
Luxembourg (2050)
Fiji (2050)
European Union (2050)
Russian Federation (2060)[1]

The website Climate Watch publishes a slightly different list:

Canada
EU (27 member states)
Iceland
Japan
New Zealand
Russia
UK[2]

Both these lists are highly questionable in that they include Russia. Climate Watch cites a government decree of 29 October 2021 for including Russia on the list. Yet the decree merely approves a strategy for Russia to reach 'low carbon emissions' by 2050 rather than net zero emissions.[3] Moreover, what value is there in any commitment on carbon emissions coming from a dictatorship which is suspected of sabotaging gas pipelines in the Baltic Sea in September 2022, releasing as much methane into the atmosphere in a few days as is emitted by the whole of Denmark in a year?[4]

Take away Russia, and the countries which have legally committed to net zero currently account for around a tenth of global greenhouse gas emissions (on a territorial basis). They exclude the world's three biggest emitters: China (32.7 percent of global emissions), the United States (12.6 percent) and India (6.9 percent).[5] Russia is often quoted as the world's fourth-largest emitter.

But for all the pledges, legally binding or otherwise, global carbon emissions continue to rise. The pandemic year of 2020, when global emissions fell by 5.4 percent, and which many people hoped might mark the beginning of the receding tide of global emissions, has already turned out to be nothing more than an aberration. In 2021, emissions rebounded strongly as economies revived – when all data has been collected it is expected to come out as a rise of 4.9 percent.[6]

What is especially remarkable is the rebound in coal consumption – an especially powerful contributor to global carbon emissions given that, per kWh, burning coal releases around twice as much carbon dioxide as does gas. Having fallen by 4 percent in 2020, global coal consumption rebounded by 4.5 percent in 2021.[7] This was not all down to China, even though expansion of Chinese coal plants was widely blamed. Electricity generators in Europe and the United States turned back to coal, too, in reaction to surging gas prices. This was especially true in Germany, which has one of the most ambitious targets for net zero, legally committing itself to eliminating net emissions by 2045. Yet a panicked decision to abandon nuclear power after the 2011 Fukushima disaster, when a tsunami flooded a reactor in Japan, has left the country stubbornly dependent on coal. Between January and September 2021, according to the energy market research group AGEB, German consumption of hard coal rose by 20 percent on the same period a year earlier and that of lignite – the dirtiest form of coal – by 26 percent. Renewable energy generation over the same period fell by 2 percent in response to a year of light winds, leaving Germany's commitment to net zero to recede agonisingly into the distance. Given the choice between making progress towards that target and keeping the lights on, it has chosen the latter.

In short, the world has tried to reduce carbon emissions by turning from dirty coal to cleaner gas, but the switch has increased demand for gas, which has consequently been driven up in price. As a result, the world has been driven into a partial return to cheaper coal. The year 2021 seemed at first to promise a breakthrough in the world's path to net zero, with more pledges than in any preceding year. But the promises quickly collided head-on with reality as countries stared at the prospect of the lights going out – and pulled back, prioritising living standards over climate action.

At some point, countries which have made pledges to reach net zero are going to have to decide how committed they are: are they going to stick rigidly to those commitments, even if it risks impoverishment of their people – or are they going to row back on their commitments and treat their targets more flexibly? Are they going to act like Britain has done so far, or take an approach more like that of China? Unless we can invent and perfect new technologies extremely quickly, something is going to have to give.

And what of the United States, the world's second-largest emitter of greenhouse gases? Under Donald Trump, it withdrew from the Paris Agreement and isolated itself from international efforts to address climate change – although its carbon emissions fell significantly as coal gave way to cheaper, and cleaner, shale gas. Joe Biden, on becoming President in January 2021, was seen by many as the leader who would put America back at the heart of global co-operation – and certainly he reversed Trump's withdrawal from the Paris Agreement. But then? Biden has a 'goal' of reducing US emissions to net zero by 2050. But that is all it is. It has not been upgraded to a legally binding target and neither does it look like being. Indeed, the President's Build Back Better framework, which he published in October 2021 and which was supposed to set the path to eliminating emissions by 2050, turned out to be far more about social issues: health, welfare and so on. As regards climate, its biggest promise was to try to ensure that wind turbine blades and solar panels 'will be built in the US with American-made steel and other materials'. It was protectionism, dressed up as climate policy.

Biden's climate measures were eventually passed by the Senate in August 2022 as part of an Inflation Reduction Act. They included $60 billion for clean energy projects, a levy for emitters of methane, tax credits for carbon capture and storage and grants for new electric vehicles. It has been claimed by an energy consultancy, Rhodium Group, that the measures will help reduce US carbon emissions in 2030 by between 31 and 44 percent on 2005 levels (compared with a 24 to 35 percent reduction already expected as a result of a switch from coal to gas and other things).[8] You can call that progress, but it is not a commitment to net zero. Nor is it quite the same as announcing that you are phasing out coal power by a certain date – which Biden conspicuously declined to do at COP26 – or declaring that you will ban fossil fuel-powered cars within the decade, as the UK government has done.

It seems pretty straightforward: for all Biden's talk of leading global efforts to reduce emissions, he intends the United States to behave a lot more like China than Britain. He isn't going to be telling the American public that they can't have this or that, or imposing open-ended costs on them by ordering them to change their domestic heating to a much more expensive alternative – and Congress wouldn't let him if he tried. All he is prepared to do is to chuck money at them – the whole Build Back Better programme has been priced at $1.75 trillion

– in order to encourage them, but not to force them, into making choices which he hopes will turn out to be greener. The cost – equivalent to $5,000 for every American taxpayer – will be borrowed and paid for by future generations.

The big emitters, the big players, then, are not going to be going down the hair shirt route. That is the preserve of Britain and a few other, mainly European, countries. But if we are, unilaterally, going to try to get to net zero just how are we going to do it, and what are the implications for ordinary households?

6.

Exporting our emissions . . .

WE KNOW WHERE WE ARE going – or where the government
has promised to take us. But how do we get there? Net zero
looks a little less of an onerous challenge if you think we are
already some way to the destination. That is one of the UK
government's strategies in trying to sell the concept to the
public: to tempt people to believe we have already eliminated
nearly half our emissions.

In his speech proposing the net zero target to the House of
Commons in June 2019, government minister Chris Skidmore
told MPs: 'The House has heard already of the great progress
we have made in tackling climate change together across parties;
of how we have cut emissions by 42 percent since 1990 while
growing the economy by 72 percent.' If we could get this far
while still growing the economy, we were invited to believe,
then getting rid of the remaining 58 percent of carbon emissions is surely little more than a mopping-up exercise.

Since 2019, according to official figures, we have inched a
little closer still: by 2021 the UK government was claiming
to have reduced greenhouse gas emissions by 43 percent
compared with 1990 levels. What ministers don't tend to admit,
however, is that this figure is an illusion, an accounting trick.
It includes only 'territorial emissions' – i.e. those physically
spewed out within the United Kingdom. It excludes emissions
from international aviation and shipping, as well as those
released elsewhere in the world in the cause of providing food

and other goods for consumption in the UK. The alternative – and fairer – way of measuring emissions is on a 'consumption basis', which includes emissions from all products and services consumed by people resident in the UK. When you study these figures – which are published rather more quietly by the UK government, using a methodology devised by the University of Leeds – you find a very different story.

The figures for UK consumption-based greenhouse gas emissions don't go back all the way to 1990 – they start in 1997, when they stood at 954 million tonnes of 'carbon dioxide equivalent' (mostly carbon dioxide but also including other gases, such as methane, which are known, or suspected, to have a warming effect on the Earth's climate). Territorial emissions for 1997, by contrast, stood at 753 million tonnes. By 2018, territorial-based emissions had fallen to 468 million tonnes, a drop of 38 percent. Consumption-based emissions also fell, but by only by 26 percent, to 703 million tonnes. In other words, not only are consumption-based emissions falling a lot more slowly than are territorial-based emissions, the former are now a full 50 percent higher than the latter.[1]

How come? Britain has genuinely cut some of its emissions, such as by replacing coal-fired power generation with cleaner renewables and gas. But it has also offshored many of its emissions. They have been shifted to South East Asia, along with the heavy industry which produces them. Between 1997 and 2018, UK manufacturing output, by value, just about held its own, rising very slightly from £184.1 billion to £187.2 billion, both at 2016 prices. However, the share of the UK economy made up by manufacturing fell from 16.8 percent to 9.9 percent.[2] Moreover, it was the heavier, more energy-intensive industries which declined the most. Between 1997 and 2021 UK steel production more than halved, from 1.6 million tonnes to 710,000 tonnes.[3] As a result, the UK now imports 61 percent of steel used in the country.[4]

What is especially disturbing about the decline of UK steel and heavy industry in general is that it is fed, in part, by taxes and levies imposed on British industry in an effort to reduce carbon emissions. Produce steel in Britain and you will have to pay, on your energy bill, the Climate Change Levy, the Renewables Obligation plus payments under the Emissions Trading Scheme. Produce steel in China and you do not need to pay any of these levies. There is a big differential in energy prices even between the UK and the EU. In 2020/21, according to UK Steel, the trade body for the UK industry, German producers were paying an average of £25.00 per MWh for their electricity,[5] once taxes and levies were taken into account, compared with £28.74 in France and £46.60 in the UK.

High energy prices are not the only reason why heavy industries are in decline in Britain – labour is cheaper in South East Asia, too. Nevertheless, it is plain to see that while carbon levies might strictly be said to be achieving their objective of cutting UK carbon emissions, they are doing so in an extremely negative way: by helping to drive heavy industries abroad. For the planet there is no net gain – on the contrary, displacing steel production from the UK, where most electricity is generated by gas, renewables and nuclear, to China, where much of it is generated by much dirtier coal plants, is helping to increase global carbon emissions.

There are alarming implications here. While in April 2021 the UK government did propose to set targets which in future will include emissions from aviation and shipping, there is still no proposal to include emissions baked into imports of food and industrial goods. As a result, the UK government has given itself a perverse incentive: the more industry it drives from Britain's shores, the closer it will approach its target for net zero carbon emissions. The only way to eliminate this incentive would be to shift fully towards using a consumption-based net zero target. But if it did that, the UK government would, at one stroke, find itself a lot less far along the road to reducing emissions than it currently claims to be.

This is a theme which will run through this book: that a unilateral, legally binding target for reaching net zero carbon emissions is not merely pointless – when Britain accounts for 1 percent of global emissions and China 33 percent – but it could actively damage the UK economy. The same will be true for any country which legally binds itself to the target of zero emissions. Some argue that this is irrelevant: by setting ourselves a strict target for decarbonisation we will incentivise the development of new technologies which will give us a head start in the economy of the future. That all sounds very worthy, but is no more than blind optimism. Net zero, when we don't yet know how to get there, is a hostage to fortune. It amounts to placing a faith in new technologies which is far from guaranteed to be rewarded.

This does not seem to worry some in power: they are prepared to take the bet. In 2019 Sir John Armitt, chair of the National Infrastructure Commission, likened Britain's commitment to net zero to John F. Kennedy's pledge in 1961 that the United States would put a man on the moon by the end of the 1960s, which as we know it succeeded in doing. But there is a big difference. Kennedy set one, clear ambition and awarded it a large but finite budget. He did not pass a law compelling the United States to put a man on the moon by New Year's Eve 1969 and invite activists to sue the government if it failed. By contrast, environmental activists have been handed the power to take the UK government to court if it fails in its net zero commitment – and they have already shown great enthusiasm for doing so, every time the government proposes an infrastructure project which activists can argue is incompatible with the 2050 target. They have already scored a couple of notable successes: in February 2020, they persuaded the Court of Appeal to block proposals for a third runway at Heathrow Airport, although this was later overturned in the Supreme Court. In July 2022 the High Court ruled that the government's Net Zero Strategy did not provide enough detail about how the target will be reached.

But this is just the beginning. As we shall see later, activists are gearing up to take up actions against governments for anything which they believe conflicts with commitments to eliminate carbon emissions. Any government which has made such commitments has created a very large rod for its own back.

Net zero isn't about developing one showpiece industry; it compels us to dump multiple established technologies and start again. We don't just have to be lucky with one technology; we have to be lucky with them all. No one should assume that if the will is strong enough then magical solutions will materialise; not if they are against the laws of physics. Less remembered is that NASA promised to follow up its Apollo missions to the moon by landing a man on Mars by 1980. It didn't, and it still hasn't, over 40 years later. Nor has nuclear fusion ever materialised in commercial form, half a century after it was touted to be the solution to all our energy needs; the technical challenges of creating the sustained high temperatures required have proved too great.

As our net zero deadline approaches, either technology will be kind to us – or we will be forced into desperate, uneconomical solutions in an effort to get there. So just how far are we, how far is there to go – and what are our chances of getting there?

7.

Power . . . at times

In spite of the UK government's boasts about falling greenhouse gas emissions we are a long, long way from reaching net zero emissions. We have picked some of the low-hanging fruit, but the harder-to-reach stuff is a long way from our grasp. What will it mean for people in Britain as the government pushes us to get there?

Let's start with energy, and electricity in particular. In July 2021 the government published its digest of energy statistics for the previous year. The headline that the government wanted us to read was that, for the first time, 'renewables' were generating more of our power than were fossil fuels.[1] If this was supposed to herald a new dawn, it wasn't to last. When the figures for 2021 were published a year later they showed an unexpected 3.6 percent plunge in the output of power from renewable sources, with power generated by fossil fuels rising by 4.7 percent – the main element of blame being low wind speeds during 2021.[2] We will go into the problem of intermittency in wind and solar energy later.

Eagle-eyed readers might have spotted an alternative headline from the two documents: that Britain's overall electricity generation capacity is static or falling. Between 2019 and 2020 it fell by 2.7 percent, from 77.9 GW to 75.8 GW. In 2021 it recovered but only by 1.0 percent, to 76.6 GW. It is remarkable to see overall generation capacity decline just at a time when the government is trying to electrify much of Britain's

43

energy consumption. It has declared that sales of new petrol and diesel cars must cease by 2030, with electric vehicles the most likely alternative. It wants sales of new gas boilers to be banned from 2035, with electric heat pumps predominating. By the end of the 2020s it wants 600,000 heat pumps a year to be installed in homes. What is going to power them all?

At present, 17 percent of energy consumed in Britain is in the form of electricity, with most of the rest in the form of gas and liquid fuels. In future, if we are going to get anywhere close to net zero, most of our energy consumption will have to be in the form of electricity. So why, when we are on the cusp of far greater demand for electricity, is generating capacity falling? Britain is closing down its coal power stations – all of which are supposed to be gone by 2024 – and has vowed to close its gas plants by 2035. But they are not being replaced like-for-like. Rather they are giving way to sporadic sources of renewable energy which are not quite making up for the lost generating capacity, and certainly not matching its reliability.

What about the claim that in 2020 the United Kingdom generated more electricity from 'renewables' than it did from fossil fuels – 43.1 percent for the former against 37.7 percent for the latter?[3] It sounds impressive (even if the renewables figure fell to 39.6 percent and the fossil fuel figure rose to 42.6 percent in 2021). Indeed, the government can claim a significant achievement: coal has largely disappeared from Britain's electricity mix, falling from 40.4 percent of generation in 2013 to just 2.6 percent in 2021. Given that coal, per kilowatt-hour, emits roughly twice as much carbon as does a gas-fired power station, it has helped bring about a large and genuine fall in emissions.

But what about those renewables? Whenever renewables are mentioned they tend to conjure images of wind farms and solar farms. Indeed, the government confirms this impression by almost always using photographs of turbines and solar panels whenever it publishes a document on energy. We are invited to believe that these, exclusively, are what renewable energy is all about. What we don't tend to be shown is photographs of the Drax power station in North Yorkshire, formerly the largest coal-fired power station in Europe, which has been converted progressively in recent years to burn wood, mainly harvested from plantations in North America – a 'biomass' power station. Yet Drax is our single biggest source of 'renewable' power, larger than any single wind or solar farm.

In 2021, 122.2 TWh worth of electricity generation was attributed to renewables (a Terawatt-hour, or TWh, being the amount of energy supplied by a trillion watts over the course of an hour). Of this, 64.6 TWh came from wind farms and 12.1 TWh from solar farms. A further 5.5 TWh came from hydropower. Those are the forms of renewable energy which might genuinely have a claim to be called zero carbon. But there is another side to 'renewable' energy which does involve carbon emissions. In 2021, 27.7 TWh of electricity was generated by burning biomass, such as at Drax. A further 7.6 TWh came from biogas, such as methane collected from landfill sites, and 4.6 TWh came from 'energy-from-waste' plants – a polite name for rubbish incinerators.[4]

Biomass has become big business in Britain, largely on account of Drax. Yet its claims to be a renewable form of energy are somewhat dubious. Burning wood, as with burning anything, does of course release carbon dioxide; quite a lot of it. Indeed, wood has a lower combustion efficiency than coal – per kWh, it releases around 10 percent more carbon than coal. According to the think tank Chatham House wood-burning in the UK releases between 13 million and 16 million tonnes of carbon dioxide a year, equivalent to that emitted by 6–7 million petrol cars.[5]

Yet when the government calculates Britain's carbon emissions it doesn't count emissions from burning biomass. How come? Because it argues that burning it is only re-releasing carbon which was removed from the atmosphere in recent times – as opposed to burning coal, which releases carbon which has been locked up in the Earth for millions of years. Implicit in this assumption is that every tree that is cut down will be replaced by a new tree. But a tree burns in a power station boiler in minutes; by contrast, it will take decades for the new tree to grow to maturity and absorb as much carbon as was released when the old tree was burned. By that time, the 2050 target for achieving net zero carbon emissions will have been and gone.

Even if you do make the assumption that growing trees and then burning them to generate power is carbon neutral, the process of cutting down trees in North America, chopping them up into pellets and transporting them to the United Kingdom still releases carbon because it uses machinery and transport powered by fossil fuels. Moreover, forestry disturbs the soil, which can release further carbon into the atmosphere.

There have been a number of attempts to calculate the lifecycle greenhouse gas emissions involved in burning wood pellets. One, led by the Massachusetts Institute of Technology in 2018, compared wood pellet-burning directly with coal-burning, using several scenarios. In one of them it assumed that the pellets would be obtained from thinning the woodland rather than clear-felling it. The calculation in that case was that it would take 52 years of forest regrowth before pellet-burning could be said to have emitted less carbon dioxide than burning coal. The study then calculated what would happen if the forest was clear-felled. In that case, it concluded, it would take 82 years of regrowth before pellet-burning could be said to be cleaner than coal-burning.[6] Both dates take us well beyond the 2050 deadline for achieving net zero.

Biomass-burning, then, can only really claim to be zero carbon if you disregard the time it takes to regrow the trees.

To put it another way, the claim of biomass to be carbon neutral ignores the fact that for 50 to 80 years there will be less carbon locked up in the form of wood – and consequently more carbon in the atmosphere – than there would have been had you left the trees alone. Yet when new trees are planted in Britain it is counted as a permanent removal of carbon from the atmosphere – it is treated as offsetting carbon emissions from other sources. The government doesn't disregard the carbon removed from the atmosphere on the grounds that the trees will eventually die and rot, releasing the carbon back into the atmosphere. Something isn't quite right here: two different standards of accounting are being applied. The government's carbon-accounting is flattering biomass. Burning wood pellets to generate electricity might be 'renewable' in the sense that you can replace the trees you have burned down and eventually grow yourself a new crop. But it is certainly not carbon neutral.

The other issue with biomass-burning is particulate pollution. It produces large quantities of what are known as PM2.5s – particles with a diameter of less than 2.5 micrometres, which have been linked with heart and lung disease. There have been warnings about particulate pollution from biomass-burning for years, not least from the UK government's own Air Quality Expert Group which estimated in 2017 that wood-burning contributed between 6 and 25 percent of PM pollution in urban areas during the winter.[7]

Particulate pollution is not so much of an issue with large incinerators operating at high temperatures, such as Drax, as they promote very efficient combustion. It is much more of an issue with open fires, wood-burning stoves and domestic biomass boilers – the last of which have been encouraged through a subsidy scheme known as the Renewable Heat Incentive (RHI). Under the scheme, which ran from 2011 until it was closed to new applicants in 2022, homeowners have received grants running into the tens of thousands of pounds – all on the grounds that their 'green' heating systems are helping to cut carbon emissions. The effect on air pollution has been disregarded. It is a similar story to what happened with diesel cars between 2000 and 2015, which were encouraged on the grounds they did more miles to the gallon and therefore cut carbon emissions – only later did policymakers realise that the promotion of diesel engines was leading to an increase in emissions of particulates and nitrogen oxides. That has been the trouble with so much environmental policy in recent years – everything has come to be seen through the prism of carbon emissions, as if nothing else mattered.

The Air Quality Expert Group made the point that if you replace a coal-fired power station with a biomass one it won't necessarily lead to an increase in overall pollution. But that is hardly the point. Coal plants have been recognised as source of foul pollution for decades. The shift to renewable energy ought to be a prime opportunity to clean up the air as well as to cut carbon emissions. Yet in truth, biomass neither cleans the air nor eliminates carbon emissions.

But even if we were minded to believe that biomass-burning is a zero-carbon source of energy and we accepted the government's claim that renewables now generate more electricity in Britain than do fossil fuels, that doesn't mean that we are halfway to decarbonising the entire energy sector – or anything like it. As already mentioned, only one sixth of energy used in Britain is consumed in the form of electricity. Heating homes is still largely done by burning gas, and most road vehicles are still powered by liquid fossil fuels – so too are aeroplanes and trains. Take energy as a whole and 13.6 percent of it comes from what the government describes as 'renewable energy'. Of this renewable energy, offshore wind accounts for 13 percent, onshore wind 11 percent, solar 4.5 percent and hydropower 2.2 percent.[8] Put all this together, and 30.7 percent of 13.6 percent of energy consumed in the United Kingdom in 2020 came from wind, solar and hydropower – in other words, just 4.2 percent of total energy came from sources which can reasonably be said to be clean, zero-carbon energy. We have nuclear power, too, a low-carbon form of energy which generated 16.1 percent of electricity in 2020 (and which we will deal with later). But we are a very long way from having an energy sector that can genuinely claim to have net zero carbon emissions. We are certainly nowhere near being halfway there – even if the government would like us to think we are.

The government has staked a huge amount on wind and solar in its efforts to decarbonise Britain's electricity grid. Addressing an online UN conference in September 2020 the then Prime Minister, Boris Johnson, spoke of Britain becoming the 'Saudi Arabia of wind', adding 'we've got huge, huge gusts of wind going around the north of our country'. A year later he upgraded his ambition to saying 'we can get to completely clean energy production by 2035'. Did he really mean all energy or did he actually mean to say just 'electricity' (which would be in line with his government's published policy)? One never really knows with Johnson. But for a man who once asserted, in a *Daily Telegraph* column in 2013, that wind turbines 'couldn't pull the skin off a rice pudding', his speech revealed a remarkable transformation. His ambitions did not quite meet up with the reality, however. It is one thing to encourage wind and solar farm owners to build their plant; quite another thing to absorb the energy into the national grid. In May 2022 wind farm owners were reported to be facing a wait of between six and ten years to get them connected to the grid, thanks to insufficient investment in reconfiguring the system.[9] If we are going to have an electricity supply based on renewables it is going to require a lot more investment in the grid than is currently taking place.

The idea that there is virtually limitless renewable energy out there for us to grab if only we want to do so is naive. Back in 2008 the physicist who was later to become Chief Scientific Advisor to the Department of Energy and Climate Change, Professor David MacKay, set himself the task of trying to calculate the renewable energy potential of the United Kingdom and compare it with the country's current energy consumption. He wasn't trying to assess the costs – merely to look at how much renewable energy could potentially be extracted from the sun, the wind, the waves and the earth if we could find an affordable and satisfactory way of doing so. His conclusion? That the United Kingdom potentially had 180 kWh per person per day of renewable energy on offer – but that it was currently using 195 kWh person per day.[10] In other words, we won't necessarily be able to move wholly to renewables even if we are prepared to pay the cost.

The greatest potential, he reckoned, came from solar farms (50 kWh per person per day) – although that would involve covering 20 percent of the surface area of Britain with solar panels. It would also require a vast amount of energy to build solar farms in the first place – a solar installation, he reckoned at the time (although technology has improved since), only produces four times as much energy during its lifetime as it consumes in its manufacture. In other words, we would have to ramp up our existing power production fantastically to make this huge array of panels. After solar came offshore wind (48 kWh per person per day), then UK-grown biomass (24 kWh), tidal energy (11 kWh) and wave energy (4 kWh).

It is possible to be critical of MacKay's analysis. His calculations for tidal energy, for example, were limited to the Severn Estuary, the Wash and Morecambe Bay when – to forget the cost for a moment – it would surely be possible to cover the whole of the UK coast with tidal lagoons or tidal turbines if we really wanted to. A more recent analysis by the University of Plymouth concluded that it might be possible to extract 34 TWh of electricity per year from marine turbines in strong tidal streams in 31 sites from western Scotland, Wales and the Channel Islands.[11] That would be the equivalent of 11 percent of Britain's current energy usage – although the current estimated price of tidal energy, at over £200 per MWh, would have to fall by three quarters in order to make it competitive.

Nor did MacKay consider floating wind turbines, which had not been proposed at the time. And his calculations were limited to Britain's potential for renewables. As he acknowledged, a densely populated country like Britain has the option of buying in renewable energy from elsewhere just as it already imports 40 percent of its food – at a cost, obviously, to its balance of payments. But then the whole point of the exercise was not to consider costs, practicalities or unintended consequences; it was simply to consider how much potential renewable energy there is out there to exploit. The results disabuse us of the notion that renewables are unlimited – even at unlimited cost.

But what about those costs? Following the surge in global energy prices in 2021 and 2022 it has often been asserted that wind and solar are now by far the cheapest ways to generate electricity in Britain. One of the most commonly quoted statistics in the summer of 2022 was that electricity generated via wind and solar is now 'nine times cheaper' than electricity generated by gas – £48 per MWh rather than £446 per MWh.[12] But this is like comparing the price of a bus journey using a season ticket with a one-off taxi fare. This claim was arrived at by comparing the prices fetched in a 'contracts-for-difference' auction of renewable energy with the 'day-ahead auction prices' for gas-generated electricity. Contracts-for-difference is a form of subsidy for the renewable energy industry which offers the owners of wind and solar plants a guaranteed, index-linked price for every MWh of electricity they sell over the next 15 years. The wind and solar operators have to bid for their contracts-for-difference, with the lowest bids succeeding.

That is a very different matter from day-ahead prices for gas-generated electricity – which is the price at which energy companies must buy their wholesale electricity at a day's notice. The price for day-ahead electricity fluctuates so much because energy companies are having to scramble to make up for shortfalls in wind and solar energy. If the following day is forecast to be sunless and windless, energy companies will have to buy more electricity and shell out far more to buy it. In the first seven months of 2022, for example, the day-ahead price for electricity swung between a low of £46.98 per MWh and £333.11 per MWh.[13] Obviously, if you are signing a deal to generate electricity at a guaranteed, index-linked price for 15 years you are going to accept a lower price than you would to generate a few hours' worth of electricity on a one-off basis. To put it another way, we are paying through the nose for gas-generated electricity because it is being used, at very short notice, to fill in the gaps when wind and solar farms are failing to deliver the goods. Gas-generated electricity would be much cheaper if we were using it to provide a more steady baseload.

So what is a fair comparison between the cost of generating electricity by wind, solar and gas? It is not straightforward to compare the costs of different forms of electricity generation because while some have lower upfront capital costs, others have lower running costs. It is relatively cheap to build a gas-powered generation plant, but then you incur the cost of buying gas throughout its life – as well as the cost of running the plant. It is enormously expensive to build a dam on a major river, by contrast, but once you have finished, the kinetic energy of the water essentially comes for free. To get around this problem, the International Energy Agency (IEA) uses the concept of 'levelised' costs – which compare the cost of every MWh of electricity generated throughout the life of a plant, taking into account construction, fuel and maintenance. The digest it publishes every five years – which assesses 243 plants in 24 countries – also assumes that carbon emissions are taxed at the rate of $30 per tonne of CO_2. It is not, in other words, a direct comparison, but one which looks at the current state of the market – in which, in Western countries at least, emissions are already highly taxed. For 2020, it put the median costs of various form of generation, per MWh, at:

> onshore wind $50
> nuclear $69
> gas $71
> solar photovoltaic (at utility scale) $56
> hydro (from river flow) $68
> hydro (from reservoirs) $72
> coal $88
> offshore wind $88
> geothermal $99
> biomass $118
> solar photovoltaic (on residential properties) $126[14]

It is true that wholesale gas prices have increased appreciably since 2020 – in June 2022 they were standing at approximately twice the level they were in mid-2020. Wholesale prices have always been volatile, but especially so during the summer of 2022 when they swung between £200 per therm, up to £550 and back down again to less than £200 by the end of September. If the IEA had been undertaking this analysis in 2022 it would have looked different (its next analysis isn't due to be published until 2025). But it should not be assumed that this would work against gas plants and in favour of solar and wind – the surge of inflation which has followed the Covid-19 pandemic has not just driven up fossil fuel prices; it has also led to a surge in prices of steel and rare metals − both of which are major contributors to the lifetime price of generating wind and solar energy. Moreover, the high price of gas in 2022 was down to a combination of factors which will surely prove temporary. The spike began with an imbalance between supply and demand which occurred as a result of economies beginning to recover from the Covid-19 pandemic. It was then supercharged by the Russian invasion of Ukraine, followed by a severe reduction in gas exports from Russia to Western Europe (by July 2022 only a fifth as much gas was getting through as before the Ukrainian invasion in February of that year). No one knows what gas prices are going to do in future − oil and gas have always been volatile commodities. If you want to make a fair comparison with the cost of renewable energy you have to look over the longer term.

But back to the IEA's 2020 analysis, which is the most comprehensive currently available. These figures are fairer, but even so, they are still not a genuine comparison between the underlying costs of various forms of electrical generation. They still flatter wind and solar because they ignore the cost of the energy storage which would be required to make it practical to generate electricity exclusively by those means. Moreover, the figures for coal and gas factor in carbon levies and other taxes applied to fossil fuels. That is not to say that carbon levies are necessarily a bad thing, if they encourage a switch to cleaner energy. But to tax fossil fuels is a choice − the taxes and levies are not part of the intrinsic cost of generating electricity by these means.

It is certainly true that wind and solar have come down sharply in price over the past decade, but this chart would look very different if we took away carbon taxes from the cost of coal and gas and added the cost of energy storage, constraint payments and back-up generation to the cost of wind and solar. Energy consumers have been largely unaware of what they have been paying for green energy because of the way that subsidies are built into energy bills – in the form of levies whose names might not mean much to most people. According to the energy regulator Ofgem, 25.5 percent of the average bill in 2021 was for 'social and environmental levies'. While this proportion will have fallen with rising bills (Ofgem no longer publishes the figure so prominently), the green energy subsidies are still active. The most prominent of them is the Renewables Obligation – a system which obliges energy companies to buy a certain proportion of their power from renewable sources, and which cost consumers a total of £6.3 billion over the year. While it is no longer used to fund new wind and solar farms, many of the contracts are still in place and will remain active for years to come. Then there is the Climate Change Levy, a tax on the gas and coal used to generate electricity, which cost a collective £2 billion. Consumers were also paying £1.2 billion towards the 'capacity mechanism', which subsidises energy storage and electricity generation which can be available at short notice to make up for a lack of sun and wind, as well as a couple of schemes to help low-income households insulate their homes and pay their energy bills.

But let's look beyond the costs which consumers are paying to subsidise renewable energy and assume that the IEA is right when it claims that the cost of wind and solar will continue to fall and that by 2050 both will be competitive enough to provide 70 percent of the world's electricity.[15] Before we can get anywhere close to the IEA's ambition a very big problem will have to be overcome, and one which in practice increases costs enormously – although no allowance was made for this in the IEA's figures given above.

The Achilles heel of wind and solar power is its intermittency. The sun doesn't shine all the time and the wind doesn't always blow. Indeed, somewhat annoyingly, sometimes the sun doesn't shine at the same time that the wind isn't blowing. Worse, this often occurs when energy demand is at its peak: at evening time during a winter anticyclone when temperatures drop below zero and demand for heating reaches its maximum. Even more inconveniently for the UK government, it happened on day two of COP26 in November 2021, when light winds stilled the nation's wind turbines and forced energy suppliers to buy power instead from the remaining coal furnaces at Drax power station, which were rekindled for the occasion. That is not a good thing to happen while you are simultaneously trying to boast to the world that you have nearly eliminated coal power and have a viable electricity supply based on renewables instead.

In theory, Britain already has enough installed renewables capacity to provide for almost all its current electricity consumption. In 2021, there were enough wind turbines and solar panels to provide 39.7 GW of power[16] – against average demand in 2021 of 38.1 GWh. But of course only a fraction of this can be delivered at any one time, thanks to the unreliability of the sun and wind. There are such times when wind and solar is generating virtually zero power in Britain. At 6 p.m. on the cold, still evening of 14 January 2022, for example, overall energy demand, at 43 GW, was above average. But wind was producing just 2.9 percent of the country's electricity, solar nothing and hydroelectric 2.5 percent. Britain was importing more energy – 12.4 percent – than it was deriving from renewables. Pumped storage was flat-out at 5.1 percent. Coal – at 3.9 percent – was generating more than wind, nuclear was producing 12.7 percent, biomass 6.4 percent and gas 52.1 percent.[17]

The UK energy market copes with periods of low wind and solar energy at present mostly by switching on gas plants when renewable energy production is low. We do have some pumped storage capacity, but as we will later see this was never designed to fill in the huge gaps created by lulls in solar and wind energy. There is a huge cost to keeping gas-powered electricity plants on standby and turning them on only occasionally. They don't work so efficiently that way, and it is necessary to pay their owners eye-watering prices to compensate them for keeping the plant idle for the rest of the time. During a period of low winds in September 2021 owners of gas plants were being paid £2,500 per MWh to take up the slack – 50 times the normal wholesale price of electricity.[18]

On the other hand there are times when wind farms are producing too much energy for the grid to digest. On these occasions wind farm operators are paid large 'constraint payments' to switch off their turbines. In 2020, consumers were forced to bear the cost of £282 million worth of these. Over the course of the year, 3.8 TWh worth of potential wind-powered electricity – 6 percent of all wind-generated power – went to waste because it could not be used.[19] Bizarrely, wind farm owners are often paid more, kWh for kWh, to turn off their turbines than they are paid when they are generating electricity.

But what will we do from 2035, when the government plans to eliminate gas from electricity generation? How will we cope with unreliable wind and solar energy then? There are two ways we can potentially deal with the intermittency problem: by storing energy when the sun is shining and the wind is blowing, for times when they are not – or else by constructing a global super-grid which exploits the fact that the sun is always shining and the wind is always blowing somewhere. Either way, it is going to add considerable cost to wind and solar energy.

First, storage. In 2014 the UK government launched what it calls the 'capacity mechanism' – which means offering subsidies to businesses which can guarantee to supply large quantities of electricity at very short notice in order to make up the shortfall in renewable energy supply. This can be done either by keeping the generating plant on standby or by building an energy storage facility. It was envisaged that the capacity mechanism would create a market to encourage the development of new storage technologies, but in practice it has proved a lifeline for old coal and gas plants which were supposed to have been retired by now but which are kept on standby for times when wind and solar energy are scarce, as discussed above. It is they who keep winning the 'capacity auctions' for the subsidies. The capacity market has kept the lights on, but it has done little to stimulate the development of new forms of energy storage.

It is certainly possible to store significant quantities of energy; indeed, we have been doing it for decades. High in a valley in the slopes of Ben Cruachan, a mountain in Argyll and Bute in the western highlands of Scotland, sits a 316-metre-long dam which holds back a reservoir of 10 million cubic metres of water. It is part of gigantic 'battery' – or pumped storage system – which works on a disarmingly simple principle: when there is surplus power in the grid, it is used to pump water up to the reservoir from Loch Awe, 400 metres below. When power is required, the water is then allowed to flow back to Loch Awe, passing through four massive turbines on its way. It is capable of storing 7 GWh worth of energy, released at a rate of 440 MW – approximately equal to the output of the now defunct Hunterston A nuclear power station which sits 70 miles away on the Firth of Clyde. Indeed, the two were designed to work in tandem. Hunterston was to generate electricity at an even pace, as a nuclear reactor is happiest. Cruachan would then help match supply and demand, by absorbing excess energy generated at night and releasing it by day.

Cruachan is one of four pumped storage power stations in Britain. No new ones, however, have been opened since the

1980s. All the while that the British countryside has been filling up with wind turbines and solar panels generating intermittent energy, not one large-scale plant has been built to store energy. Another pumped storage plant has been proposed on Loch Lochy near Fort William, but work had yet to start by the beginning of 2022. Investors have shown little interest in further projects – in spite of high peak prices being offered to the operators of pumped storage systems. The payback time for pumped storage has been estimated at 40 years – too long for most investors. One of the problems is connection costs; suitable sites for pumped storage systems tend to lie a long way from where demand for electricity is greatest. Building dams, too, is a pretty expensive business. Moreover, you don't get back all the electrical energy you put in – only around 75 percent of it.

The US Department of Energy in 2020 estimated the lifetime cost of energy from a pumped storage system at around $131 per MWh.[20] That was around twice the wholesale price of electricity in Britain at the time. We keep being told that the price of generating electricity from wind and solar is now as cheap, if not cheaper than, coal or gas, but that is misleading. To assess the full cost of wind and solar power you have to take into account the cost of storing some of the energy until it can be used. And the cost of storage, it turns out, is at least twice as expensive as generating the electricity in the first place.

Britain boasts of being ahead of other countries in renewables, offshore wind in particular. But it is a long way behind in energy storage. Britain has a total of 39.3 GWh of energy storage, mostly pumped storage.[21] Given that we consumed 346,000 GWh of electricity in 2020 this amounts to just 60 minutes' worth of supply. Imagine for a moment that the nation's electricity was supplied entirely by wind and solar. If the Cup Final was held on a dull and windless day, you wouldn't even get as far as the second half before your television flickered and died.

What about using batteries to store energy? The UK electricity industry has been experimenting with them – but again nothing on the scale as in some countries. There is no lack of ambition in the global giant battery industry. When not selling electric cars, Elon Musk's company Tesla is making lithium batteries to help energy grids balance supply with demand. In 2017 the company installed the Hornsdale Power Reserve to run in tandem with the Hornsdale Wind Farm, a 99-turbine facility in South Australia operated by French-owned power company Neoen. When fully charged it can store 194 MWh of electricity, which it can discharge at a rate of 150 MW. That's a lot of electricity, but it is nevertheless just 37 minutes' worth of the output from the adjoining wind farm when it is operating at its 315 MW capacity. That may be fine for what the batteries are designed to do: smooth out diurnal peaks and troughs during favourable periods of weather. In October 2021 the battery installation helped South Australia get by on wind and solar power for 29 days, helped by mild weather which reduced power demand. But it is no solution for the problem of slack weeks and months, when the wind might not blow strongly for days on end.

Nor does the installation appear to have been fully successful in the other task for which it was designed: preventing blackouts when there is a problem with other power plants; indeed, in 2021 the operators were being sued by the Australian Energy Regulator for failing to help prevent outages when a coal plant suddenly failed. Big batteries come with their own risks. An even bigger battery installation in neighbouring Victoria, the Victorian Big Battery, had its opening delayed in July 2021 when a large fire broke out in one of its containers. The fire involved 150 firefighters and 30 fire engines, and it took six hours for the fire in the battery packs to burn themselves out

– exposing a well-known problem with lithium batteries.[22] Obviously, any kind of engineering involves risk, but this is an issue which will have to be resolved if we are going to build large numbers of battery installations, especially if they are in built-up areas. Australian wildfires have been claimed by many people in recent years as a symptom of climate change (more on that later), but it will not look good if a battery fire sparks off one of these conflagrations.

The advent of lithium ion batteries represented a big leap in battery technology. But if we are going to store electricity week from week, month from month, we are going to need more than marginal improvements; we are going to need another huge step-change in technology. The problem at the moment is that storing energy in batteries costs even more than storing it in pumped storage plants – nearly three times more, at around $336 per MWh. We are forever being told that wind energy has become a bargain as costs have fallen, with each MWh costing us under £50. But if you have to spend five times this cost to store much of the energy until such times as you can use it, it ceases to look even affordable.

Could there be a technology which could turn that around, so that storing the energy becomes a fraction of the price of generating it? There are plenty of people and resources being poured into that problem, looking at various possibilities. There are putative efforts to store energy in salts. There are two large plants, one in Germany, one in the United States, which store energy by using surplus power to pump compressed air into underground chambers, then release it through turbines when electricity is needed. There is another possibility in the form of thermovoltaic storage, where surplus energy is used to heat rocks, or other materials, to extremely high temperatures, to be turned back into electricity when required. There is a company, Antora Energy, trying this now at the Lawrence

Berkeley National Laboratory outside San Francisco, heating up pieces of carbon to 2,000 degrees Celsius.

Some have suggested employing the batteries of electric cars to store energy for the grid – thereby reducing the need for giant storage facilities. When wind and solar farms are failing to produce much electricity, we could draw down energy from the nation's cars instead. But there is a slight problem with this solution: what if you need to drive somewhere and you find your car battery has been drained to feed a hungry electricity grid in the night? You can use energy stored in a car battery to help back up the grid, or you can use it to drive the car – you can't use it for both on the same day.

Could we turn to hydrogen – using surplus electricity to produce hydrogen from electrolysis of water when there is plenty of renewable energy, and using it either to produce electricity when renewable energy is scarce or using it to heat homes or power vehicles? The UK government has put huge faith in hydrogen as part of its decarbonisation plans, and a number of private companies have proposed projects to use hydrogen in this way. It may well become a large part of the solution one day, but for the moment manufacturing hydrogen by electrolysis remains extremely expensive – as we shall see in the next chapter. Consultancy ERM has an idea to couple a 4 GW floating wind farm in the North Sea with an electrolysis plant which would turn sea water into hydrogen.[23] Tractebel, a subsidiary of energy company ENGIE, plans to generate hydrogen from wind farms and store it in caverns at 180 bar below the bed of the North Sea.[24] There are also proposals to store hydrogen in tanks on the bed of the North Sea.

But with all these technologies the biggest issue is cost. The Pacific Northwest National Laboratory has attempted to calculate the levelised cost of various forms of energy storage (the cost per unit of energy stored, averaged over the life of the plant, including capital and running costs). At 2021 prices, and assuming that the plant is designed to discharge its stored energy over a ten-hour period, it comes out as:

Compressed air	$104 per MWh
Pumped storage	$131 per MWh
Hydrogen	$203 per MWh
Lithium ion batteries	$336 per MWh[25]

The study also attempted to forecast the costs in 2030 – after, hopefully, technology has improved. This is a mug's game, as we know, but it is interesting that the researchers expect only hydrogen and lithium ion batteries to fall appreciably in cost – to around $152 per MWh and $244 per MWh respectively. Even then they would still be more expensive than the pumped storage systems we already have. The study also noted that while compressed air seems to have a huge cost advantage over the others, it depends on a very particular geological formation of underground cavern – and that these are sparse. There is, in other words, little on the horizon to suggest that costs of storing energy are going to come down dramatically any time soon.

Compare these costs to the price of generating the electricity in the first place – described earlier in this chapter – and you can see just how expensive energy storage is. And of course the cost to store energy comes on top of the cost of generating it – you are paying twice. Even in the best-case scenario – generating electricity via onshore wind and then storing it in the form of compressed air – we would be paying $154 for our stored, renewable energy ($50 for generating the energy and $104 for storing it). That is nearly double what we were paying for gas-generated electricity in the summer of 2021, even taking carbon levies into account. Does the huge inflation in gas prices since the summer of 2021 change the figures? When wholesale gas is as expensive as it was briefly in August 2022 it certainly looks attractive to build a grid based on wind and solar backed up with some kind of energy storage. But that was a brief spike in wholesale gas prices, which by October 2022 were back to where they had been in the early summer of that year. Compared with the longer-term average of gas prices, wind and solar backed up by energy storage is a very expensive option. Moreover, the surge in inflation which has followed the Covid-19 pandemic hasn't just affected oil and gas prices; it has affected most commodity prices, which in turn have begun to feed through into the cost of building wind and solar farms, and even more so the cost of making batteries. If we are going to live with a grid powered mostly by wind and solar, and without the backup of gas, power is going to be very cheap on windy and sunny days – and extremely expensive on sunless and windless ones. This is something consumers are likely to feel in a very direct way. In its blueprint for a decarbonised future, published in 2021, National Grid ESO proposes to deal with the problem of intermittency in wind and solar through what it calls 'dynamic containment' – using smart meters in order to charge variable prices throughout the day in response to supply and demand.

But could we do without mass energy storage? What about the possibility of a worldwide electricity grid, which would work on the principle that it is always sunny and windy somewhere? If we could link up the world's renewable energy then we wouldn't need to worry so much about storing large quantities of energy – we could shift it around the globe to where it was needed.

We already do have international electricity interconnectors, which allow electricity to be imported and exported in order to exploit different patterns of supply and demand. Britain has been linked to the French national grid since 1986, and other connections have been added since so that, as of 2021, Britain can, at any one time, exchange 3 GW of power with France, 1 GW each with Belgium and the Netherlands and 500 MW with Ireland. To put these figures into context, Britain's electricity consumption averaged 38.1 GW in 2021. Between 2018 and 2021, a 1.4 GW cable was laid between Britain and Norway, a metre below the seabed. At 450 miles it is the longest such link in the world. The rationale behind that £1.5 billion project was that Norway has the potential to supply surplus hydroelectric power – while Norway hopefully might be able to consume surplus UK wind energy at times.

We do, then, already have an embryonic international electricity grid. But Britain, France, Belgium, the Netherlands and Norway are all within one time zone of each other, providing limited opportunities to exchange solar energy. If Britain is going to try to live on renewables it is going to have to think a lot bigger. One company is doing this. A start-up called Xlinks has proposed to lay a cable from Morocco to Devon, southwest England, capable of delivering 3.6 GW of power to the UK national grid. The electricity would be generated by a vast solar and wind farm covering 600 square miles, with batteries to try to smooth out supply. The facility would take advantage of the more reliable and more intense solar energy available in North Africa, as well as frequent winds blowing onshore from the Atlantic.[26]

But transporting electricity long distances doesn't come cheap. The cost of the Morocco–UK cable, together with the wind and solar farm, has been estimated by the company at £16 billion. That, notionally, would work out a little cheaper than building a large nuclear power station – the latest estimate for Hinkley C power station in Somerset (which is designed to produce 3.3 GW of power) is £23 billion. But there are large uncertainties. Never has such a long electricity cable been laid, and the water between Morocco and Britain is far deeper than the North Sea. There is also the matter of transmission losses, which in the case of the Norway to UK cable have been put at around 5 percent.[27] In other words, send 100 GWh worth of electricity from a Norwegian hydro-electric plant to Britain and you will only get 95 GWh worth at the other end. A Morocco to UK cable would be four times as long, so you would expect to lose around four times as much energy along the way – leaving you with only around 80 GWh of your 100 GWh. The bigger the grid, the more electricity you try to transmit across the world, the more these losses will matter. Could we lay transatlantic cables to take advantage of solar energy once the sun goes down in Europe and North America? That would be a minimum of 3,500 miles and 15,000 feet deep in places – and be half as far again as a Morocco–UK link. The transmission technology will have to improve if we are to avoid losing a third of our energy on the transatlantic journey. That is another project to file away under 'possibilities', whose costs and practicalities have yet to be tested.

If we are to have an international electricity grid, governments will have to get used to the idea of being dependent on other countries' generators and the need to keep them free from political interference. That is something which some are struggling with at present. In October 2021 the French government threatened to cut off the electricity supply from the island of Jersey in a dispute over fishing licences.[28] Three months later the UK government was reported to be blocking the deployment of a third interconnector between Britain and France on the grounds of energy security – it didn't want to become more dependent on French power[29] – although the link did open in 2022. If we are going to have a global electricity grid, we are going to have to accept the loss of energy security and put up with the risk that in an emergency, other countries could decide to block the export of power.

But assuming we did find an affordable way of powering

large parts of our economy by wind and solar it ought to be emphasised that even these energy sources are not wholly zero carbon − not yet at any rate. They require large quantities of steel and concrete for their construction; industries which are themselves very carbon-intensive, or at least will be until anyone succeeds in developing commercially proven means of producing both commodities without carbon emissions − not easy, as we shall see later. The carbon intensity of electricity from a wind turbine (taking into account whole-lifecycle emissions, including manufacture and operation) is not huge compared with other forms of electricity generation. Estimates have varied from 5 grammes of CO_2 per kWh for an onshore turbine in Europe to 25.5 grammes for an offshore turbine in China − compared with 400–700 grammes for gas-generated electricity and 700–1,700 for coal.[30] But if we are really going to get to net zero, all emissions are going to count. Even at 5 grammes of carbon dioxide per kWh − equivalent to 5 tonnes of carbon dioxide per GWh − a UK electricity grid powered entirely by wind, were that possible, would still be responsible for 330,000 tonnes of carbon dioxide emissions a year. That might be a small proportion of the emissions from fossil fuel-generated electricity, but it shows the difficulties in trying to get all the way to net zero carbon emissions. It is simply not possible without some means of achieving negative emissions, the costs and practicalities of which we will go into later.

There is another issue which needs to be addressed before we can hope to become the Saudi Arabia of wind: declining global wind speeds. In 2021, Danish wind energy producer Ørsted had to issue a profit warning as a result of unexpectedly low wind speeds throughout the year, leading to less electricity being produced. Most of that can be put down to one year's weather, yet wind speeds have been on a downward trend throughout much of the northern hemisphere for several decades, up to a latitude of 70 degrees north. Only above this latitude are wind speeds generally increasing. Declining wind speeds – or 'stilling' – is an aspect of climate change that we rarely hear about, perhaps because the evidence directly contradicts the lazy assertion continually made that climate change is giving us more extreme winds (in common with more extreme everything).[31] Wind turbines themselves slow down the wind by extracting its energy. This becomes rather important when we are trying to cover entire landscapes with wind turbines – a mass of turbines will generate considerably less electricity than an isolated turbine, 80 percent less according to a study by the Max Planck Institute for Biogeochemistry.[32]

There is a form of renewable energy which should be inherently more reliable: namely hydro and tidal power. As David MacKay's aforementioned study noted, the potential for hydro electricity from rivers in Britain is not great. Tidal power, however, is another matter. Britain is surrounded by strong tidal flows which, although not constant, complement each other because they are staggered in time. Tides on the Severn at Weston-super-Mare, for example, are six hours behind those on the Thames at Tilbury. By placing tidal stations around the coast we could balance supply in such a way as to produce more or less constant output. Unlike sun and wind, tides can be predicted years in advance. Moreover, tidal barrages could double up as flood defences – which are going to be necessary to cope with rising sea levels.

All that said, a government feasibility study in 2010 pretty well dismissed the case for a tidal barrage on the Severn on the grounds of cost and environmental damage. It looked at several options, the best-value of which was a barrage between Weston-super-Mare and Cardiff which it said would be capable of generating 15.6 TWh worth of electricity a year – equivalent to 5 percent of total UK consumption in 2020. But the project would cost £34.3 billion (at 2010 prices).[33] The levelised cost of electricity would be £312 per MWh – around six times the market price of electricity at the time. Not only that, the barrage would disrupt the tides in the Severn, leading to the loss of 30 species of bird and cause a population collapse of fish, including the local extinction of some species.

Subsequently, plans emerged for a tidal lagoon in Swansea Bay, which would generate around a quarter as much power. That was granted planning permission in 2015 but the government later withdrew support, again on the grounds of cost. The plans for both projects have not entirely gone away, but for the moment tidal power – the most reliable form of renewable energy we could hope for – is going nowhere in Britain.

Barrages are one way of harnessing tidal power. The other is simply to install subsea turbines much like wind turbines, except smaller and stubbier. This is a potentially cheaper way of extracting tidal energy. There is also wave energy: devices which can extract energy from the bobbing up and down of the surface of the sea. There is no shortage of engineers trying to harness energy from the sea. In early 2022 the European Marine Energy Centre was listing 97 current projects around the world to harness tidal power and over 250 projects to harness wave energy.[34] Much of this work has been going on for years, and in some cases decades, yet none has yet been commercialised. One of the closest to achieving this is a pair of turbines known as Orbital O2 installed off the Orkney Islands, northern Scotland, which began generating power in July 2021. They are designed to deliver 2 MW of power, exploiting some of the strongest tidal currents off Britain.[35] While a promising technology, it is still a demonstration project which may or may not prove economical in the long run.

Maybe some or all of the technologies we need to decarbonise electricity will break through, but we are now entering the realm of the not-yet-possible – of technologies which work in theory, or work in the laboratory, but which have yet to show that they can be scaled up into an economical form. It may be that in years to come technology will advance so fast that renewable energy, combined with energy storage, becomes so cheap that it really is cheaper than using fossil fuels – at which point there will be no need to rig the electricity market in its favour – we simply won't need fossil fuels any more. If that happens, then great. But for the moment, for all the grand ideas whizzing around, we are still hugely reliant on gas-generated electricity to balance intermittent solar and wind. Moreover, the overall generating capacity of the UK grid is falling just at a time when we are supposed to be embarking on a huge switch to electrifying homes and transport – and our self-imposed deadline of reaching net zero by 2050 is marching up on us in very real time.

8.

Nuclear

IF EVER THERE WAS A cautionary tale against excessive faith in the advance of technology it is provided by Lewis Strauss, Chairman of the Atomic Energy Commission in the United States, who told the National Association of Science Writers in New York in 1954: 'It is not too much to expect that our children will enjoy in their homes electrical energy too cheap to meter.' Did he have nuclear fission or nuclear fusion in mind? I guess his children could yet live – just about – to see a revolution in nuclear fusion, and warm their ageing toes beneath electric blankets which cost virtually nothing to run. But atomic scientists will have to get a move on.

The failure of nuclear energy to fulfil its promise has not been for want of trying. The world's first fission plant at Windscale, Cumbria, began feeding energy into the UK grid in 1957, three years after Strauss spoke. Another 65 years on and nuclear energy has managed to grow and hold on to a 10 percent share of global energy generation – including a 16 percent share of UK generation in 2019. Yet accidents at Three Mile Island in 1979, Chernobyl in 1986 and Fukushima in 2011 have helped to prevent it becoming the mainstay of electricity generation. So, too, have stubbornly high costs. The UK government only managed to persuade French energy company EDF to commit to building a new plant at Hinkley C in Somerset by guaranteeing the company a price of £92.50 per MWh at 2013 prices, rising with inflation, for 35 years.

That was around twice the wholesale price for electricity at the time – although with the surge in electricity prices in 2022 it begins to look a bargain, at least for now.

If Strauss was talking about nuclear fusion, that is even further away from providing us with free energy. Seventy years of research and development, and many billions of pounds of taxpayers' money, have failed so far to deliver an experimental plant which produces more energy than it consumes. The high, sustained temperatures required to fuse the atoms of hydrogen isotopes to create a helium atom have proved too much of a challenge. The closest we have yet come is the JET experimental nuclear fusion plant which in 1997 succeeded in producing, very briefly, 16 MW of power, but only thanks to 25 MW of input power used to maintain the very high temperatures – 150 million degrees Celsius – required for fusion to occur. It is like trying to keep yourself warm with a fire only to realise you are having to work so hard with the bellows that you are generating more heat energy from your muscles than is produced by the flames.

Will nuclear fusion ever get there? Twenty-five years on from its 1997 breakthrough, JET set a new record, this time sustaining 11 MW of power for five seconds.[1] By 2025 we should have a bigger and better demonstration plant, the International Thermonuclear Experimental Reactor (ITER) being built in southern France. That is designed to produce 500 MW of power for an input energy of 50 MW – which would at least prove that fusion could be a viable source of energy. But we will have to wait until 2025 to find out whether it is really possible. But even if ITER does succeed in producing more energy than it consumes, we will still only be halfway to a viable power station. To achieve that, fusion will have to prove itself economically, too: that it is capable of generating electricity of greater value than the cost of producing it. According to the UK Atomic Energy Authority we might expect a commercial nuclear fusion power station around 2040.[2] For its part, the International Atomic Energy Agency believes that nuclear fusion is more likely to be a solution for the end of this century.[3]

Strauss was showing the same hubris that has become common in the debate over net zero. Miracle technologies are forever on the cusp of being developed, according to the optimists, and they will turn out to be far cheaper than the fossil fuels they replace: just set a date to phase out carbon emissions and the market will surely deliver all the solutions. Except, that is, if it turns out to be like nuclear fusion, in which case we could still be shivering long after the government has mandated net zero carbon emissions. Such is the potential prize of nuclear fusion – which could theoretically produce large quantities of energy from small amounts of sea water and lithium – that it is still worth pursuing. If it were to work commercially it could blow all other renewable energy out of the water; the wind turbines would go to rust. But it is a vain hope that it could help us decarbonise by 2050.

All this said, it is hard to imagine us getting anywhere near net zero without nuclear energy being at least part of the answer. In contrast to wind and solar, nuclear fission plants can at least provide energy continuously and reliably. Yet it would take an extremely sharp change in policy merely for nuclear energy to keep up where it is now, let alone deliver the huge uplift in generation which would be required to provide the energy needed for electric cars and heat pumps. In 2022 two of Britain's remaining seven nuclear power stations were closed. The latest projected opening date for Hinkley C is 2026, which would be nine years late. But on its own it won't even replace the four nuclear stations which are scheduled to close by that date. By 2035, all five existing power stations are projected to reach the end of their working life. Will there be any more, after Hinkley C? In July 2022 the government approved plans for a third nuclear plant at Sizewell, Suffolk. There are discussions about a new plant at Bradwell, Essex. But Hitachi has abandoned plans for a new plant on Anglesey, North Wales, and Toshiba has pulled out of a proposed plant in Cumbria. In March 2022, with the much-neglected issue of energy security suddenly thrust back into national debate, the UK government quickly published an energy security strategy which floated vague proposals for another eight large nuclear power stations. Yet there was scant explanation as to how these would get built anything like in time to help Britain reach its net zero target.

Any government wanting to expand nuclear energy in Britain will have to overcome a big political problem. It is noticeable how all proposals for new nuclear reactors in recent years have been on sites adjacent to existing nuclear power stations. Any attempt to build them elsewhere is bound to run into extremely strong opposition, not all of it unreasonable. While nuclear power generally has an excellent record and even the cataclysm of Chernobyl, caused by an explosion in a reactor of a design which would never have gained permission in the West, killed fewer than 50 people directly (plus a much-argued-over number of people who died of elevated rates of cancers over the following years), the economic cost of a nuclear accident in a country as densely populated as Britain would be devastating. For all the hyperbole, climate change is a long way from causing the evacuation of a city, but the Chernobyl disaster did just that: the Ukrainian city of Pripyat, which was abandoned shortly after the 1986 accident. Draw the same 30-kilometre exclusion zone around Hinckley C as was drawn around Chernobyl – and which remains virtually uninhabited even now – and it would mean evacuation of the towns of Bridgwater and Taunton, as well as the centre of Cardiff, across the Bristol Channel.

Think it couldn't happen in a developed country? Chernobyl

was an especially dangerous design, built without a containment vessel, and would never have been sanctioned in Britain. But it would be foolish to dismiss the risk of a serious accident, either in a power station itself or in the handling of radioactive waste. A 20-kilometre exclusion zone had to be drawn around Fukushima after it was inundated by the 2011 tsunami. Britain is not in a seismically active region, but it does seem somewhat perverse to be building nuclear power stations in low-lying coastal locations when you are simultaneously warning about rising sea levels. True, the rise in sea levels predicted by the IPCC for the year 2100 is only of the order of half a metre, which would not threaten the Hinckley site, but 110 miles away on the west coast of Wales residents of the village of Fairbourne have been told by planners that their village will be 'decommissioned' later this century because it will become impossible to protect it from erosion caused by rising sea levels – leading to claims that they will become the country's first 'climate refugees'. Meanwhile, we build a nuclear power station in a vulnerable seafront location, supposedly to tackle that self-same climate change. Something isn't quite right here. Either we are facing inundation, beyond our ability to cope, or we are not.

The government's hope for nuclear power lies partly in small modular reactors (SMRs), which could be built at lower cost in factories and be transported to site, and which would also allay some of the fears over safety. They would have a lower risk of overheating; and even if the worst did come to the worst, the consequences of a disaster would be far smaller. Modular nuclear reactors could even be built underground to lessen the spread of radiation in the event of an accident and to protect them from military attack. Rolls-Royce is developing two designs which it hopes might be supplying power as early as 2029. They would each produce between 220 MW and 440 MW of power – equivalent to around a tenth of

Hinkley C or around 100 of the largest current wind turbines. According to the International Energy Agency (IEA) there are 72 such designs for SMRs being worked on globally, of which it expects 25 to exist as demonstration projects by 2030.[4] Small nuclear reactors have been in use in submarines for decades, where they have the advantage of being able to operate for months on end without requiring large quantities of fuel or needing air for combustion. The Soviet Union tried a design of SMR for civilian power in the mid-1970s but abandoned it a decade later. In 2019, Russia deployed a floating SMR in the Arctic. China is experimenting with SMRs of between 100 and 200 MW for use in district heating systems in cities.

SMRs are a very promising area of new technology. But, as with so much in the pipeline of net zero, this is a technology at a developmental stage and no one knows whether these plants really will turn out to be economical to build or run. They provide no confident basis for a target of removing all fossil fuel-based electricity generation from Britain's national grid by 2035. No form of nuclear energy yet invented marries well with an electricity system built on intermittent wind and solar. You can power gas-fired power stations up and down reasonably quickly in order to fill the gaps when the wind is not blowing and the sun is not shining. But nuclear power stations don't work like that – in order to work efficiently and safely they need to be run at a fairly constant level of output.

As in Britain, the global nuclear industry is currently stalled. In 2020, 6 GW of new capacity was brought online, but 5.4 GW was removed. Globally, there is a total of 58 GW worth of new nuclear power projects under construction, but again there are plenty of older stations due to be decommissioned in coming years. France, which embraced nuclear energy like no other and which at present generates 70 percent of its electricity in this way, is now planning to reduce this to 50 percent by 2035, while increasing renewables. Germany, which once generated a quarter of its electrical power from nuclear energy, has been closing them following a hurried decision by former Chancellor Angela Merkel in response to the Fukushima disaster in 2011. On current trends, estimates the IEA, global nuclear generation will grow from 415 GW now to 582 GW by 2040.[5] That is not going to get anywhere close to replacing fossil fuels – and unless there is a decisive reduction in costs as SMRs prove themselves, that picture is unlikely to change.

9.

Homes and heating

In the 2019 report which inspired the UK government to commit itself to a legally binding target of net zero carbon emissions by 2050, the Climate Change Committee (CCC) – set up by the government to advise it on such matters – bolstered its case by citing an opinion poll from a year earlier. The Opinium poll recorded that 64 percent of adults 'agree that the UK should aim to cut emissions to zero over the next few decades'. But none of those who replied could have known what the CCC has in store for them – their homes especially. Even now, few UK homeowners are aware of what is about to hit them.

The CCC has since put some meat on the bones of its proposed timeline for Britain to reach net zero by 2050. It has recommended that installation of new gas boilers in domestic properties should be forbidden from 2033 – with either electric heat pumps or hydrogen boilers suggested as possible alternatives. As for new oil-fired boilers, which are the main form of heating for homes in rural areas without a mains gas supply, they should be banned from 2028. The CCC also demands higher standards of insulation for buildings, as defined by Energy Performance Certificate (EPC) ratings. From 2028, it recommends that it should be illegal either to sell or rent a home with an EPC rating below 'C'. From 2033, all properties with a mortgage would have to have at least a 'C' rating.[1]

The government has already adopted some of these ideas. Its Heat and Buildings Strategy, published in October 2021, confirmed an intention to ban all new gas boilers from 2035. Installation of new oil boilers would cease in 2026, two years earlier than the CCC suggested. The document makes it clear that the government favours electric heat pumps as the main alternative to fossil fuel-powered boilers – it wants 600,000 of them installed every year by the end of the 2020s. Otherwise, the plan is a little vague on dates, but it does set out a time-line showing that from 2035 all existing homes must conform to EPC rating 'C' or above 'where practical, cost-effective and affordable'.[2]

In 2019, the CCC recognised that enforcing a switch to low-carbon heating would swamp households, especially low-income ones, with huge bills. 'It would be regressive, and probably restrict progress, to pass the cost on fully to house-holds,' it stated.[3] A year later it had changed its tune. Now, it expected households to bear the cost of transforming their homes. But it wouldn't cost all that much, it tried to reassure us. The total cost would be £250 billion by 2050, working out at less than £10,000 per household. Moreover, 63 percent of homes would have to 'spend no more than £1,000 on retrofitting energy efficiency measures'.

Is that really likely? The Energy Savings Trust – a govern-ment quango set up to advise the public on how to save energy – suggests that a ground-source heat pump costs between £14,000 and £19,000 to install in a typical three-bedroom home (assuming the space was available for the underground pipes, which it isn't in the case of most homes). A cheaper option, a less efficient air-source heat pump, would cost between £7,000 and £13,000.[4] But the bills don't end there. Most heat pumps currently available work at lower temperatures than do traditional heating systems powered by gas boilers, and require homes to be well insulated if they are to work effectively. They may also require underfloor heating and/or much larger radiators to be installed. Improved insulation will certainly be required for existing homes to be brought up to a 'C' rating on an EPC. At present, only 42 percent of homes in England and Wales have a rating of 'C' or above.[5] Around 8 million homes have solid walls and so cannot easily be fitted with cavity wall insulation. In these cases, homes would have to be fitted either with internal wall insulation – at a typical cost, according to the Energy Saving Trust, of £8,200 for a three-bedroom semi-detached house – or external wall insulation (which would typically cost £10,000 for the same property).

Heat pumps which work at higher temperatures are gradually becoming available. These produce water at between 65 and 80 degrees Celsius – in the range of a traditional gas and oil boiler – rather than between 35 and 40 degrees Celsius for a standard heat pump. They do, therefore, provide a potential alternative in older buildings which are difficult to bring up to modern standards of insulation. There is, however, a price to pay. They cost around 25 percent more than a standard heat pump and are markedly less efficient. While a well-functioning standard air-source heat pump will have a Coefficient of Performance (COP) of three – meaning it will deliver three times as much heat energy into the home as electrical energy it consumes – high-temperature models have a COP of between 2 and 2.5. The running costs, therefore, will be considerably higher.[6]

On the above figures, it would cost a minimum of £7,000 to replace a gas boiler with a heat pump. Add in wall insulation (forget for a moment floor insulation and any other improvements) and the bill will rise to a minimum of £15,000 for a modest three-bedroom house. Or, if you want to go for a high-temperature heat pump you could do without the extra insulation but spend a minimum of

£10,000 (and suffer higher heating costs). For many homes the cost will be far higher. So why is the CCC telling us that it will cost most homeowners less than £1,000 to decarbonise their properties? It is possible that the cost of installing a heat pump will become cheaper as the industry becomes established, but there is scant sign yet of prices tumbling. The government's Net Zero Strategy, published in October 2021, declared the aim of 'making heat pumps as cheap to buy and run as a gas boiler' by 2030 at the latest.[7] But where did that wishful thinking come from? In 2019 the CCC forecast that the cost of a heat pump would fall only as far as £5,800 by 2050 – still more than twice what a gas boiler costs to install today (which the Energy Savings Trust puts at £2,300). Whether a heat pump ends up cheaper to run than a gas boiler depends on the future price of electricity. Heat pumps, as the Net Zero Strategy admits, currently cost more to run than a gas boiler. In 2022 the Energy and Utilities Alliance, a trade body for the gas industry (a not entirely disinterested body), put the annual average cost of heating a home on gas as £984, against £1,251 for a heat pump.[8] What hope that electricity prices will fall in future? Pretty unlikely, given that gas power stations will be phased out by 2035 and intermittent renewables installed in their place, meaning extra costs involved with providing energy storage.

Could it be economical to install district heating systems, where multiple properties are heated using one central ground-source heat pump, thus – hopefully – utilising economies of scale? District heating systems can be an economical means of providing heating in dense urban areas, such as Copenhagen. The city of Nottingham has had a district heating system, using waste heat from a municipal rubbish incinerator to heat 5,000 homes, since 1995 and has had some form of district heating since 1874. But in low-density suburbs and rural areas the economics are very different. The Cambridgeshire village of Swaffham Prior has never been on the gas grid – as it has never been considered economical to lay gas pipes to its low-density streets. Most homes there in recent decades have been heated with oil-fired boilers – new installations of which are due to be banned from 2026. That is why the village was chosen as a test bed for a district heat-pump system, which was installed in 2021 offering hot water at up to 72 degrees Celsius to the 300 homes in the village. But the economics stack up even less well than they would have done for putting the village on the gas grid – a lot less, in fact. If every home signed up for the new heat pump network it would work out at £40,000 per home. As at December 2021, however, only 47 households had signed contracts – meaning that the £12 million public-funded cost of the scheme worked out at over £250,000 per property. If we spent £40,000 replacing the heating of all 27 million homes in Britain at this price it would cost £1.1 trillion. That alone would exceed the Climate Change Committee's estimate for reaching net zero by 2050. True, costs might be expected to come down if the technology was rolled out across the country and installers worked out how to do the job better, but the Cambridgeshire project is not 20 percent too expensive, not 50 percent too expensive, it is ten times more expensive than installing each home with an oil boiler.

And, of course, switching homes from fossil fuel boilers to heat pumps – whether individually or on a district heating scheme – does not, in itself, decarbonise them. All it does is to convert them to being heated by electricity – nearly half of which at present is still generated by fossil fuels. The struggle to decarbonise the electricity grid is proving hard enough as it is, but it would be a lot harder still were the grid forced to provide enough energy to heat every home in the country. According to Ofgem the average UK home on the gas grid uses 12 MWh worth of gas a year. If we can be optimistic and say that all homes could be replaced with heat pumps capable of delivering three times as much heat energy into a home as they consume in electrical energy, it means each home would need to draw an extra 4 MWh of electricity each year. Multiply that by the 27 million homes across Britain and it means we would need an extra 108 TWh. In 2019, the UK consumed a total of 346 TWh of electricity, so if every home were to run on a heat pump it would increase electricity demand by around a third. That is an awful lot extra of wind turbines, solar panels – and energy storage too.

So much, then, for the idea that we could all spend £1,000 greening our homes and enjoy lower bills to boot. It is astonishing that the Climate Change Committee was ever allowed to get away with this claim. Its bizarrely optimistic figures on energy efficiency costs feed into its overall estimate for Britain to reach net zero by 2050: the £1 trillion of investment by 2050 that was quoted at the beginning of this book. The CCC's estimate for decarbonising homes – £250 billion – was a full quarter of this sum. Look at the Energy Saving Trust's figures and you can see it is inevitable that the eventual bill is going to be far higher than this. Gradually, this does appear to be seeping into the consciousness of MPs – the same MPs who nodded through the 2019 commitment to reach net zero by 2050. As the House of Commons Public Accounts Committee – a body made up of MPs – put it in a report in March 2022, the CCC has based its figures on a series of 'heroic assumptions' with 'errors potentially compounding over very long periods'.[9]

Aside from the satisfaction of thinking they have done their bit to cut the nation's carbon emissions, what will householders actually get for this outlay? Will a heat pump even keep you warm? Field trials of heat pumps conducted by the Energy Saving Trust between 2008 and 2013 were far from encouraging. A well-functioning heat pump ought to have a Coefficient of Performance (COP) of three – that is to say it can pump three times as much heat into a house as electrical energy it consumes. If the COP is less than three, heating your home with a heat pump is going to cost significantly more than heating it with gas. Yet the COP of the 22 air-source heat pumps in phase one of the trials varied between 1.2 to 2.2 – in other words, none of them was up to standard. The 49 ground-source heat pumps did a little better, but still many of them underperformed horribly – their COP ranged from 1.55 to 3.47. In a second phase of the trial poorly performing pumps were subjected to remedial work, ranging from fitting extra valves to complete replacement. Yet even after all that, only 20 out of 32 performed better. Still, most failed to achieve an COP of three. The air-source heat pumps had a range from 2.0 to 3.6 with an average of 2.45 and the ground-source heat pumps had a range of 1.6 to 3.8, with an average of 2.82.[10]

Manufacturers and installers have had nearly a decade to improve their products since then, and some customers report being happy, yet still tales abound of people who have been dissatisfied by the ability of their heat pumps to keep them warm. Broadcaster John Humphrys, for example, says he spent 'a small fortune' installing a ground-source heat pump at his Welsh home, but that after all that the device 'takes the chill off the downstairs rooms but that's about it'.[11] So, we have a policy of switching millions of British homes from well-functioning gas- and oil-fired boilers to a system of heating which doesn't seem to work well in many cases, costs much more to install and also costs more to run. And that is at current electricity prices, where half of the country's electricity is generated by gas. Once gas power stations are phased out and we have to employ energy storage on a massive scale to cope with inter-mittent renewables it is hard to see how electricity prices are going to do anything other than rise. How many owners of old properties would voluntarily choose to spend thousands replacing a well-functioning gas boiler with a heat pump if they could not be sure it would keep their house warm, and would increase their bills? Heat pump technology is not at a stage at which it would sell itself. Rather it is being forced upon the public in the knowledge that it will do a much less-good job for a lot more money than will a gas boiler.

There is a potential alternative to heat pumps: hydrogen boilers. These would likely work out cheaper to install than heat pumps. It is possible that the existing gas mains could be repurposed to carry hydrogen, which would further limit the amount of investment required to decarbonise home heating. This doesn't mean, however, that a hydrogen heating system would be cheaper to run than would a heat pump – as we shall see. Moreover, there are a number of serious problems which would have to be overcome first.

The government certainly hasn't held back in its enthusiasm for hydrogen, which it says could account for between 20 and 35 percent of UK energy consumption by 2050. 'A booming, UK-wide hydrogen economy could be worth £900 million and create over 9,000 high-quality jobs by 2030,' declared business secretary Kwasi Kwarteng, launching his hydrogen strategy in August 2021, 'potentially rising to 100,000 jobs and worth up to £13 billion by 2050'.[12] Let's skate over the unfortunate use of the word 'booming' – perhaps best avoided in the context of hydrogen. I do love the conceit that these are going to be 'high-quality jobs' as if the gas industry didn't also create well-paid employment. Being a hydrogen worker, evidently, is a cut above being a mere gasman.

To listen to the hype you would think that someone had tapped into a huge underground chamber of hydrogen which, as with gas, you can exploit by more or less sticking a pipe in the ground and pumping it off down the street to homes and businesses. While there are cases of freely occurring hydrogen being found in geological formations, no one has yet succeeded in exploiting it nor identifying a significant reserve which could potentially be exploited. Therefore, as yet, hydrogen is not a fuel in the sense that coal, oil or gas is a fuel. It is merely a store of energy. It first has to be manufactured, the process of doing which is extremely expensive and itself consumes energy.

The attraction of hydrogen is that its combustion releases no carbon dioxide, nor any other noxious chemicals – just water vapour. But that doesn't necessarily mean that it hasn't spewed out some carbon along the way. The trouble is that at present virtually all hydrogen produced in the world is manufactured from fossil fuels – 76 percent from gas, 23 percent from coal – with the result being that its manufacture emits vast quantities of carbon dioxide. It stands to reason there is no point in installing a hydrogen boiler to cut your domestic carbon emissions to zero if somewhere over the horizon is a hydrogen plant doing the emitting instead.

It is possible, however, to capture some of the carbon dioxide produced by the hydrogen manufacturing process and pump it underground, where hopefully it might stay forever after – a process known as carbon capture and storage (CCS), which we will look at in greater depth later on. Hydrogen produced in this way is known as 'blue' hydrogen. But the technology available at present won't remove quite all the carbon dioxide produced in the process – about 10 percent will remain, at best. If you are really going to reach net zero emissions, heating homes with blue hydrogen will not get you there – you will need some additional way of removing carbon from the atmosphere.

There is a cleaner way of manufacturing hydrogen: via electrolysis, using electricity to split hydrogen from water molecules. This is what is known as 'green hydrogen'. The technology to do this does exist – indeed, it has been known about for nearly a century – but it has not previously been used to manufacture hydrogen on an industrial scale because it is not very efficient. It currently costs around three times as much as producing hydrogen from methane. At present, according to the International Energy Agency, only around 0.1 percent of hydrogen produced globally is green hydrogen. The problem is that if you use electrical energy to manufacture hydrogen you lose around a third of the energy along the way. But the losses don't end there. In order to transport this naturally low-density gas through a pipe network it is first necessary to compress it – a process which consumes around another 13 percent of the energy contained within the hydrogen itself. By the time your 'green', electrolysis-produced hydrogen has reached your boiler you have lost much of the energy with which you started. According to an analysis for the US Department of Energy's Alternative Fuels Data Center, if you produce hydrogen by electrolysis and then distribute it by pipeline, for every unit of energy delivered to the home you will have consumed 2.12 units of energy in the production and distribution process. In other words, you will have less than half the energy that you started with. By contrast, refining and distributing oil consumes approximately 12 percent of the energy that you started with.[13]

This might not matter so much if we could use surplus wind and solar energy to produce the hydrogen. At the moment, we are turning off wind turbines on windy days when the grid can't consume all the electricity they are producing – and compensating wind farm owners for doing so. But how about using surplus energy to generate vast quantities of hydrogen on sunny and windy days, store it in tanks or underground caverns and then pump it into homes to be used whenever it is required?

If we were able to use electricity which we couldn't

otherwise use, then it would change the economics – yet hydrogen power still comes out as depressingly expensive. Figures produced by the UK government in 2021 looked at the levelised cost of producing hydrogen by various means (this includes the capital cost of the infrastructure as well as running costs and fuel). Producing blue hydrogen from methane (with carbon capture and storage) was put at £60 per MWh. Producing green hydrogen via electrolysis, by comparison, was put at a minimum of £180 per MWh. The study also estimated what it might cost to produce hydrogen from surplus wind farm-produced electricity which couldn't otherwise be used. Discounting the cost of the electricity all the way to zero brought the cost of the hydrogen down to £60 per MWh.[14]

That is the most likely role for hydrogen in future: as an expensive way of storing energy from wind and solar farms which we couldn't use in any other way. But there is no way that conversion from gas boilers to hydrogen boilers is going to do anything other than to cost householders a lot of extra money. In the summer of 2021 (before a spike in response to a surge in global demand) wholesale gas prices in Britain were hovering around £20 to £25 per MWh. By the summer of 2022 that had risen to £60 per MWh – a level which was considered to have precipitated a cost-of-living crisis. That price takes into account current carbon levies and yet still comes out at no more expensive than green hydrogen using 'free' surplus electricity from wind farms.

Could technology bring the cost of hydrogen down? The government doesn't seem to hold out a lot of hope for that. Its projections show the cost of green hydrogen only coming down to £50 per MWh by 2050. That might just about bring it within the realm of affordable energy, but it is highly speculative. Estimates such as these are no basis for a legally binding commitment to reach net zero by 2050. As for blue hydrogen

– which the government says it is keen to promote as a halfway house to green hydrogen – it sees prices as being pretty flat right out until 2050. It stands to reason that blue hydrogen is always going to cost significantly more than natural gas because it uses gas as its raw material – and it can't possibly be cheaper to manufacture a fuel from a fuel than it is simply to burn the gas in the first place.

Moreover, not everyone is convinced that blue hydrogen is a cleaner way of heating buildings than burning gas – or even coal. An analysis by Cornell and Stanford Universities calculated that greenhouse gas emissions from burning blue hydrogen could be 20 percent greater than those from plain natural gas or coal. Heating a home with blue hydrogen, they found, would emit less CO_2 compared with heating the same house with gas, but it would be responsible for greater methane emissions. The study assumed that 3.5 percent of natural gas escapes in the form of fugitive emissions during production. Given that blue hydrogen requires a greater amount of gas to deliver the same energy, the greater fugitive methane emissions more than cancelled out the drop in CO_2 emissions. The study was based on real-world data from a blue hydrogen plant which showed it capturing between 53 percent and 90 percent of CO_2 emissions.[15]

If we are going to convert homes to hydrogen heating there is also the issue of safety to consider. On a disused airfield at Spadeadam in Cumbria, northern England, stands a row of three houses which have been built by engineers to assess the operation of hydrogen boilers – in particular the propensity for leaks. The fact that they are four miles from the nearest habitable property gives a clue as to what the issue is here: hydrogen, as amply demonstrated by the Hindenburg disaster in 1937, is highly flammable. So, too, is natural gas, and every year a number of homes are demolished by ignition from gas leaks. But hydrogen is potentially even more dangerous – not least because the small size of molecules allows the gas to escape from smaller fissures. An analysis by the consulting engineers Arup estimates that conversion of UK homes from natural gas to hydrogen could result in the annual number of deaths and injuries in domestic explosions rising from 17 to 65 – although the risk could be mitigated by installing extra valves.[16]

Personally, I think we probably could handle the risk of hydrogen in homes. We have, after all, lived with hydrogen before. Prior to the arrival of natural gas in the 1960s, homes were lit and powered by 'town gas' manufactured from coal – and which was 50 percent hydrogen. Boilers could be installed externally – hydrogen, being lighter than air, disperses very well in the open – or in rooms with ceiling-level vents. Hydrogen also has the unfortunate effect of causing the embrittlement of steel, leading potentially to the failure of mains pipes. That, like the risk of hydrogen leaks in homes, is a problem which can be managed, but it is one more cost which needs to be added on top of a very expensive form of delivering energy.

But say we did bring the cost of hydrogen down so that we could heat a home at the same price that we can heat it with a gas boiler at present. Would that then give us zero-carbon homes? Unfortunately not, unless we can also solve the problem of leakage. The trouble is that hydrogen is itself a secondary greenhouse gas. Free hydrogen in the troposphere reacts with hydroxyl radicals, causing perturbations in the distribution of methane and ozone, adding to atmospheric warming. According to a study by the Massachusetts Institute of Technology in 2006, if we replaced all fossil fuels with hydrogen and 1 percent of that hydrogen leaked into the atmosphere (an all-too-likely scenario given the tiny size of hydrogen molecules), the effect on global warming would be 0.6 percent of that caused by current fossil fuel-burning.[17]

That is in addition to any greenhouse gas emissions from the manufacture of the hydrogen itself. Could hydrogen help reduce greenhouse gas emissions? Yes. But could it eliminate them altogether and allow us to reach zero emissions? Not quite, it seems. As with hydrogen, as with so many areas of the economy, there are multiple layers of problems to be resolved until we can reach the absolutist target of net zero. And we only have 27 remaining years to solve them.

We have looked at forms of heating, but could we insulate our homes so well that they don't need much heating anyway? Could we end up saving money in spite of using more expensive fuels than we do now? That is the assumption on which people rely when they try to tell us that we can achieve net zero at, essentially, zero cost. It is certainly possible to insulate homes so that they consume a lot less energy to heat than the typical home does today, but there are huge problems and costs associated with upgrading insulation in older homes.

Build a house from scratch and you can design the insulation as an integral part of the structure; indeed, it would be silly not to. Who wouldn't want a warm home that costs less to heat? Well-engineered new homes can use very little energy at all. Homes built to the German *Passivhaus* standard aim to use only 'passive' forms of heating such as household appliances, the heat produced by human occupants and 'solar gain' from sunshine beaming in through the windows. They also employ a heat exchanger to extract heat from the air leaving the building in order to warm air being drawn into the building through the ventilation system. Done properly – with adequate ventilation to avoid overheating and damp – and it can be a thing of wonder, although it doesn't come cheap.

Retrofitting old buildings to improve their energy performance is a wholly different matter. There are ways of bringing period houses up to modern standards by stripping them back to the bare walls and effectively building a new house inside.

But that comes at huge cost and is far from what the Climate Change Committee has in mind when it demands a rapid programme for all homes to be brought up to the standard of an Energy Performance Certificate rating 'C'. Rather, it has the notion of sending in teams of insulation workers to perform a quick fix – trying to make a proverbial silk purse out of a sow's ear.

How does it work in practice? Real-world trials of rapid insulation schemes have hardly provided a ringing endorsement. In 2011, eleven leaky old homes in Bath and North East Somerset were given the once-over in a study by the Centre for Sustainable Energy, their solid walls insulated either inside or out. Most of the residents reported their homes feeling more comfortable afterwards, but did they use any less energy heating their homes, which after all was the whole point of the exercise? Only in four of the eleven homes did the occupants end up using less energy during the winter following the work than they did in the winter beforehand. In four others there was no discernible change in energy usage. In the remaining three the outcome was mixed: two reported using less gas but resorting to their electric fires a little more and in the other one it was the other way round – they used less electricity but a little more gas. Moreover, the winter before the work was done was especially cold – December 2010 was the coldest December in at least 100 years and possibly for 400 years. The winter following the work was, as the report recognised, a lot milder. There were other problems reported, too – in one case the occupant noticed an increase in condensation.[18] In other words, in spite of spending £8,000 to £10,000 per home, the exercise saved very few emissions and very little money in running costs. One of the Centre for Sustainable Energy's suggestions was that householders could be tempted to install solid wall insulation on the back of other benefits, such as that covering their outside walls with render might make them look nicer – something which is rather in the eye of the beholder.

The Grenfell Tower fire, which killed 72 people in June 2017, was an object lesson in the dangers of allowing climate change concerns to override all else. When built in the early 1970s the West London block was purposefully designed with all public areas, including the exterior of the building, finished in non-flammable concrete. There was a very good reason for this. Tower blocks like Grenfell were built with only one stairwell, with limited means of escape – so it was absolutely vital that no fire be allowed to take hold in the common parts of the building. Councils used to ensure this through strict rules, even down to banning doormats outside people's homes.[19] But come the climate change agenda, all that went out of the window. The idea of retrofitting social housing tower blocks with insulation and cladding was born in a policy document published by the then Labour government in 2010, two years after the Climate Change Act was passed. Setting a target to reduce carbon emissions from homes by 29 percent by 2020, it envisaged a rapid expansion in the home insulation business, with an extra 65,000 jobs.[20] Moreover, the social housing sector was to lead the way. The document didn't specify that the retrofits could be completed using flammable materials – that was a failing committed by Kensington and Chelsea council along with many other local authorities and contractors as they tried to enact the policy – but neither did it mention safety. Subtly, housing policy was turned away from fire-prevention and focused instead on mitigation of climate change – with fatal results.

Astonishingly, the government is promoting the use of high-rise timber buildings as a means of tackling climate change at the same time that owners of flats with small amounts of timber cladding, or balconies made from wood, are being told they face bills of thousands of pounds to remove it. The

Net Zero Strategy published in autumn 2021 promises to 'promote the safe use of timber in construction', declaring that timber has the 'lowest embodied carbon of any mainstream building material'. In May 2022 housing minister Lee Rowley visited a six-storey timber-framed building under construction in Shoreditch, East London, and declared it to be 'an excellent example of the benefits timber buildings can bring'.[21] Meanwhile, just a couple of miles away in Islington, residents of a shared-ownership block of flats were being told that they faced bills of £30,000 each to remove timber cladding from their homes after the block failed an 'External Wall Survey'.[22] So are timber buildings safe or a death trap? The government has tied itself in such knots over its net zero commitment that its left hand no longer seems to have a clue what its right hand is doing.

The Coalition government elected in 2010 set its own strategy to improve the energy efficiency of the nation's housing stock by retrofitting them with insulation, but that, too, ran into problems. Introduced in 2013, the Green Deal offered loans to homeowners to fit insulation and undertake other improvements, with the repayments added to the property's energy bills for years to come. There was a 'golden rule' that the projected energy savings from the work must be greater than the loan repayments. And that is where the scheme tripped up. While some relatively cheap and easy improvements – like fitting loft insulation or cavity wall insulation – were found to pay their way, the same wasn't true for solid wall insulation. External wall insulation was found to save homeowners around £250 a year in energy bills, but the repayments on the work were costing £1,000 a year. The sums for internal wall insulation were a little more favourable, but still the repayments were costing £700 a year. The whole scheme was pulled by the government in 2015.

But what about the planet? A damning report by the

National Audit Office (NAO) in 2016 concluded that 'Green Deal finance has saved negligible amounts of CO_2'.[23] Public-funded insulation schemes have, however, left behind an unwanted legacy. Linda Griffiths of Carmarthenshire insulated her home using a parallel scheme called the Energy Company Obligation (ECO) – which offered grants towards energy improvements, funded by energy companies who in turn passed the burden onto their customers' bills. She received £10,000 towards the £30,000 cost of fitting external wall insulation to her home.[24] Rather than making her home warm, lowering her bills and cutting carbon emissions, it led to horrendous damp problems which she claims have taken £100,000 off the value of her home. In the Welsh district of Rhondda Cynon Taff 280 homes had to have cavity wall insulation removed after it was found to have caused damp and mould.[25] Many property owners have had much better experiences with retrofitted insulation, but trying to compel many millions of homeowners to spend large amounts of money on a form of home improvement which can go drastically wrong is asking for trouble. You can almost hear the cowboys already licking their lips at the riches that will be coming their way.

Interestingly, in its most recent report, the Climate Change Committee seems to have gone a bit cool on solid wall insulation. 'There remains uncertainty over the balance of costs and benefits for wall insulation in solid walled homes in particular, as well as levels of public support,' it reads – although it goes on to say that it still expects 250,000 homes a year to have the treatment, with 3.4 million fully insulated by 2050. It suggests that homes which don't have solid wall insulation could be brought up to a 'C' rating by other means.

But do Energy Performance Certificate (EPC) ratings mean anything anyway? Not according to the building industry people who responded to a government consultation in 2020.

Asked 'what evidence do you have relating to the reliability of EPC assessments', just five out of 145 replied that reliability was 'good'. EPC ratings notionally resemble the energy ratings given to washing machines, fridges and dishwashers, but with a very important difference: whereas appliance manufacturers can easily obtain an accurate measure of how much electricity their products consume, EPC ratings are arrived at via computer modelling, using assumptions made by a surveyor. In practice, they are little more than guesswork. I have seen it for myself. I had two EPCs done on my house in the early days of the certificates. The first gave me an 'E' rating. Over the following year I doubled up the loft insulation, upgraded some of the double glazing and had another EPC undertaken. This time I was given an 'F' – i.e. my house had apparently declined in energy efficiency. I have seen two flats in the same block, one given a 'B' rating on the grounds there was 'wall insulation (assumed)' and one given a 'D' on the grounds there was 'no wall insulation (assumed)'. One developer spent £10,000 renovating a flat, putting in insulation and replacing the gas boiler with electric heating – only to see his EPC rating fall from B to D – meaning it could no longer be let from 2028 onwards. The assessor who carried out the second survey suggested that he take out the electric boiler and put back a gas one because it was a cheaper form of heating and would thus earn a higher rating.[26]

In other words, the whole EPC system is working counter to what the government and the Climate Change Committee want to achieve. The government is threatening us with the prospect of being unable to sell – or mortgage – our homes, unless they have a high EPC. Yet technology to reduce carbon emissions is in practice being rewarded with a lower EPC rating.

In any other context, loading costs on people of limited means would be considered an outrage. Yet when it comes to the climate, very different rules seem to apply. Remarkably, some of the same people who one day raise concerns about 'fuel poverty' will, the next day, in the context of climate change, argue in favour of an energy policy which would make it far more expensive for people to heat their homes. Policy is driven by panic, and desperation to reach the arbitrary target to reach net zero by 2050. It is one thing to demand high energy-performance standards from new homes; but to enforce the decarbonisation of properties built many years ago to very different standards threatens to impose huge costs on people who have already struggled financially to afford to gain a foothold in Britain's horribly over-inflated property market.

10.

Transport

THE ELECTRIC CAR IS THE pin-up of net zero. If books and magazine articles on the subject are not illustrated with pictures of wind turbines, they are likely to carry images of a car being recharged. Ownership of an electric car is one of the ways in which individuals like to show off their green credentials, such as Grant Shapps, the former UK transport secretary who has on occasions boasted of his Tesla – while admitting that he also owned a Chrysler Crossfire (a gas-guzzler which returns a mere 27 miles per gallon).[1] The UK government's proposed ban on new petrol and diesel cars from 2030 is one of the best-known measures to have impinged on the consciousness of the British public, argued over incessantly on internet forums and in private conversation.

If you are going to try to reach net zero emissions, there is some justification for making road transport a priority. In 2016, direct emissions from road transport (which doesn't include, for example, the manufacture of the steel to make vehicles) accounted for 11.9 percent of total global greenhouse gas emissions. This dwarfs emissions from aviation (1.9 percent), shipping (1.7 percent) and rail (0.4 percent). Together, transport accounted for 16.2 percent of emissions.[2] Moreover, there are reasons why you should want to promote zero-emission vehicles: they improve air quality, at least in the places where they are driven – although, depending on how the electricity used to power them is produced, they might merely be transferring some emissions from one place to another. I certainly have no emotional attachment to the internal combustion engine – I would much rather drive an electric car were it economical and practical.

Choose your statistics carefully and Britain is already heading full-speed towards full electrification of its road vehicles. In December 2021 it was reported that sales of new battery-electric vehicles had doubled in a year, from 10,345 to 21,726, and that plug-in vehicles (which includes hybrids as well as pure-electric vehicles) now accounted for 28.1 percent of the market for new cars.[3] Were that to continue, the government would not have to worry about meeting its target for banning new petrol and diesel cars by 2030; we would all have gone electric well ahead of that date.

But is all what it seems? The same figures show that overall car sales for the month of November were running at only two thirds of the level they were in the same month of 2019, before the Covid-19 pandemic. Meanwhile, the prices of second-hand cars were soaring. What is happening is that a lot of motorists are clinging on to their old cars. They don't want to buy a new petrol or diesel car, perhaps worrying that it would be banned from the road before it reached the end of its life. But neither, in many cases, do they want to buy an electric car.

It isn't hard to see why. First, there is the purchase price. To take some of the best-selling electric cars in Britain at the end of 2021, the Nissan Leaf cost a minimum of £26,995 new and the nearest petrol equivalent, the Micra, £16,675. The Hyundai Kona electric version cost £27,950 and the petrol version £21,265, the Kia Ceed electric £30,395 and the petrol version £20,105. As a general rule of thumb, electric cars in recent years have been costing around half as much again as their petrol equivalents – and that is when you take into account the government grants available to buyers of lower-priced electric cars. Subtract these grants – which the government abolished in June 2022 – and the gulf between petrol and electric cars is even greater.

In the Panglossian world of net zero, costs are always on the point of falling dramatically. In May 2021 Bloomberg claimed that the cost of new electric cars would be on a par with petrol ones by 2027.[4] By December it was claiming this would happen by 2024.[5] Meanwhile, the prices of metals used in the manufacture of car batteries were heading in the opposite direction. The prices of lithium carbonate from China rose by 300 percent over the course of 2021, and the price of cobalt hydroxide by 80 percent. As a result, by November Chinese manufacturer BYD was warning that it would have to increase the prices of its electric vehicles by 20 percent.[6] By February 2022 the rising cost of minerals had begun to afflict Tesla, too; it was switching production of its standard-model cars from nickel-based lithium ion batteries to lower-specification lithium iron-phosphate ones – with the effect of reducing the range of the cars.[7] And then, in one day in March 2022, in response to Western sanctions against Putin's Russia, nickel prices doubled. Given that the average electric car uses nearly 30 kg of the metal, the rise in price of nickel over the year had added more than $2,750 to the cost of producing a vehicle.[8] Is it just a spike caused by a crisis? No one can really predict the prices of commodities in three years' time – if they could they would become extremely wealthy, extremely quickly – but it is foolish to assume that prices of raw materials and finished products will always fall just because we would like that to happen. The rise of electric vehicles over the past decade has coincided with a period of relatively low commodity prices. Electric cars are finding themselves on a very different cost trajectory now that the good days seem, for the moment, to be over.

Could lower running costs change the equation, and negate

TRANSPORT

the higher purchase price of electric cars? That is what many advocates of electric cars claim: that you pay more upfront but will more than recoup it over the long term because, mile for mile, it costs less to run a car on electricity than it does one on petrol. The consumer organisation *Which?* has provided a – neutral – comparison. For a Peugeot 208, the petrol version costs £22,210 and the electric one £27,875 – a difference of £5,665. However, over three years – assuming annual mileage of 9,000 miles – the petrol one will cost £4,395 to run and the electric version £1,849. On that basis, the owner of the electric vehicle would start to save money after around six years.[9]

However, there is a very big caveat to put on these figures. They compare the current costs to consumers, but they do not reflect the genuine costs of running the cars. That is because they ignore the enormous differential in tax. The electric car, at the time the *Which?* comparison was published, qualified for £2,500 grant towards its purchase. It incurs no road tax and – if the car is charged at home – the user will pay no duty on electricity other than 5 percent VAT. The petrol car qualifies for no grant, is liable for annual road tax of £155 (and a higher rate for the first year) and its fuel is heavily taxed: around 60 percent of the price of a litre of fuel is tax. While this might mean that an electric car seems cheap to run now, it is inconceivable that, as electric cars become more commonplace, the Treasury will sit back and watch as the £28.4 billion revenue it currently raises in road fuel duty and the £6.5 billion it raises in road tax evaporates. At some point, it is going to act to make up for the lost revenue by imposing new motoring taxes; indeed, the Chairman of the National Infrastructure Commission has already proposed a national road-pricing system which would see cars tracked and charged for every mile they drive.

In other words, if you are assessing the cost of running an

electric car you really need to factor in the – as-yet unknown – cost of future motoring taxes. Alternatively, let's compare the ex-tax costs of running a petrol car versus an electric one. So let's adjust those *Which?* figures and put petrol and electric cars on a level playing field – i.e. ignore taxes/grants and look at the underlying running costs. The tax on a litre of petrol (assuming a price of £1.50 per litre, as it was in August 2021 when the *Which?* article was published) is 58 pence fuel duty and 25 pence VAT – a total of 83 pence. Drive 9,000 miles in a petrol car which does 10 miles to the litre and you will be using 900 litres and paying £747 a year in fuel taxes (900 litres multiplied by 83 pence). On top of this, you will pay £155 a year in road tax. Subtract these taxes – a total of £902 a year, £2,706 over three years – and the (ex-tax) cost of running a Peugeot 208 for three years falls to £1,689 (4,395 minus 2,706).

In the name of fairness, let's also subtract from the cost of running an electric car the 5 percent VAT paid on recharging an electric car at home. According to its official energy consumption figures, a Peugeot 208 consumes 0.257 kWh per mile (in real life many motorists have found their cars under-performing in this respect). In 9,000 miles it will consume a total of 2,300 kWh. Assuming electricity at 20 pence per kWh – and VAT at 1 pence per kWh – that means the electric-car owner will be paying £23 a year in VAT to recharge the vehicle, or £69 over three years. Ex-tax, then, the three-year cost of running the electric Peugeot 208 comes down to £1,780 (1,849 minus 69). In other words, ex-tax, running the petrol car in reality costs less than running the electric one – without the tax advantages you would never recoup the higher purchase price of the latter. And, of course, the differential in purchase price is, in reality, much higher than that stated by *Which?*, because the taxpayer is contributing a grant – £2,500 at the time *Which?* did its analysis, later reduced to

£1,500 and removed altogether in June 2022. Leave out the grant, and the electric Peugeot 208 would have cost £30,375 – nearly half as much again as the petrol version.

The figures, of course, change all the time. In the months following the *Which?* article there was high inflation in fuel prices, with the average petrol price hitting 180 pence by June 2022. This led some to claim that the economics had shifted even further towards electric cars and away from petrol and diesel ones. Yet that rather ignores that the surge in energy bills had hit electricity prices, too. In April 2022 the energy price cap on electricity bills – used by the government to protect customers for high bills (although ultimately it cannot defend against large rises in wholesale costs) – rose by a third, from 21 pence/kWh to 28 pence/kWh. Percentage-wise, that was a bigger increase than had hit petrol and diesel in the previous six months.

But leaving aside the costs, are electric cars even practical? There are two issues with which owners of electric cars are still struggling: range and the difficulty of recharging their vehicles. It is easy to be seduced by the theoretical range of premium electric cars. The Tesla Model S is now being advertised with a range of 400 miles – but then it costs £95,000. For most people the reality is a car that will do fewer than half this number of miles between charges. Take the base model Nissan Leaf, which costs new a slightly more affordable £25,000. It is advertised as having a range of up to 168 miles. But the 'range calculator' on the Nissan website explains how this would be reduced in real-life conditions. Fill the car with passengers and luggage and drive at motorway speeds while the outside temperature is 5 degrees Celsius and the range drops precipitously to 99 miles.[10] But it is only possible to do that number of miles if the car is charged with a slow charger, which takes 7 hours 30 minutes. Use a rapid charger – which takes 60 minutes to charge the battery from 20 to

80 percent full – and you can only take the battery to four-fifths capacity: i.e. sufficient to travel 80 miles under the conditions described above. Several times a year I drive to the Scottish Highlands in a diesel car which packs in 800 miles on a tankful. I could do the 440-mile journey in under eight hours, but with generous stops it takes around ten or eleven hours. And in a Nissan Leaf, according to the manufacturer's figures? If I started fully charged, I could perhaps risk travelling 80 miles before I needed to recharge for the first time. Thereafter, if I used rapid chargers I would only be able to do 60 miles between charges. I used the website zap-map.com, which locates chargers, to plot a route. It was going to take me a minimum of seven charges, each taking half an hour of charging time – plus whatever it took to locate the charger, and perhaps to wait for it to become available and hook it up. And that was assuming that everything went as it was supposed to. At points on my journey, according to the website's calculations, I would be down to just 17 percent charge, and several of the sites had only one suitable charger. If it wasn't available I would be in serious trouble, with no chance of getting to the next site.

That the charging network is at present hopelessly inadequate to serve a Britain with fully electric cars is at least acknowledged by the government. In July 2021 – with less than nine years left before the sale of new petrol and diesel cars is due to be banned – the Competition and Markets Authority (CMA) laid out just how far there is to go before we have a practical charging network. It projected that Britain would need to have between 280,000 and 480,000 public charging points if all cars were to go electric. But at present there are only around 25,000 (although zap-map.com puts it higher, at 34,000 charging points).[11] In practice, though, many motorists find it impossible to use a great number of these. Many charging points require subscriptions – only 9 percent could be used simply with a credit or debit card. They use four different kinds of connector, with many vehicles only compatible with one kind. They are concentrated in cities, leaving many remote areas as 'charging deserts' – density varies between 80 charging points per 100,000 population in London to just 20 in Yorkshire and Humber. Few are in convenient locations for the 8 million households where cars cannot be charged because they have no driveway or off-street parking. Outside London, according to the CMA, there are just 1,000 on-street charging points to cover the entire country. Rapid-charging points on motorways – essential to long journeys – are especially sparse as well as expensive. Long-term monopolistic contracts mean that providers can charge 60 percent more for electricity compared with charging at home (the latter being the price used in most efforts to compare the costs of running an electric car with a petrol one). Moreover, found the CMA, one in ten rapid charging points on motorways are out of action at any one time.

Will the charging network improve in time for the proposed ban on new petrol and diesel cars from 2030? It will have to start getting a lot better very soon. Between January and September 2021, according to the Society of Motor Manufacturers and Traders, 212,181 new plug-in cars were purchased, and 4,109 chargers were added to the system – a mere one for every 52 cars.[12]

But never mind the chargers, what about the electricity? If we are going to switch Britain to electric vehicles within the next decade something dramatic is going to have to happen to the country's generating capacity. In 2019, road vehicles in Britain used a total of 35.6 million tonnes of oil equivalent (a measure which adjusts for the different calorific values of various liquid fuels and which is defined as the amount of energy released by burning a tonne of crude oil). One tonne of oil equivalent is itself equivalent to 11.63 MWh of energy, which puts the total energy consumption of fossil fuels by road vehicles in 2019 at 414 TWh. By comparison, the UK electricity industry generated 325 TWh worth of electricity in 2019.[13] Electric vehicles are more efficient at converting electrical energy into kinetic energy than are petrol or diesel ones – around 75 to 80 percent of energy contained in their batteries reaches the wheels, compared with around 30 percent of energy contained within the fuel of a petrol car. Then again, around 10 percent of the electricity generated in power stations is lost on its way to the consumer and more will be lost charging up the battery of an electric vehicle. But either way, switching to electric vehicles is going to increase massively the demand for electricity – as is ditching gas boilers in favour of domestic heat pumps. And if we are going to reach net zero, all this extra electricity is going to have to come from renewable energy or other low-carbon sources. That is an awful lot more wind turbines and energy storage, plus huge investment in the electricity grid – all of which means a lot of extra cost.

Unless there is a dramatic fall in the cost of buying electric cars, or in the cost of electricity, it is hard to see how Britain can possibly switch to electric vehicles without imposing significant extra costs on motorists – and, indeed, forcing many of them off the road. Some people will not see that as a bad thing, foreseeing a cleaner and more pleasant future in which our towns and cities are not choked with cars. One such person who appears to hold this view is Trudy Harrison, a former junior transport minister, who told a conference in December 2021 that owning a car is 'outdated 20th-century thinking' and that we need to be moving towards 'shared mobility' – i.e. public transport and pooled-use cars that we hire by the hour.[14]

But if a carless nirvana is what you want, you should be honest about the consequences. The reality is that the switch to electric is likely to favour the wealthy, who will be able to afford the extra costs and will be able to enjoy driving on emptier roads, and disfavour the not-so-wealthy. Electric cars are fine for doing a lot of short journeys in urban areas, but then these are the sort of journeys which might be better done by public transport, on bike or on foot. They are a lot less suitable for sparsely populated rural areas, where it is unlikely to prove economical to install a network of rapid chargers.

For the past six decades our towns, cities and countryside have all been developed on the assumption of mass car ownership. Much of our housing stock is in locations which can only readily be accessed by car. The same is true of many shops, workplaces and leisure facilities. If Britain were to be reconfigured for 'shared mobility', it would take many decades to reverse past planning decisions. Moreover, there is little sign that we are even heading in that direction. Even when we are supposed to be preparing for a future of net zero carbon emissions, housing developments are still being built in locations where it is difficult to live without a car. The Royal Town Planning Institute analysed large housing developments granted planning permission between 2015 and 2019 and found that on average it would take twice as long to reach shops, schools, hospitals and other amenities by public transport as it would by car. The average journey to a secondary school, for example, was 13 minutes by car, 30 minutes by public transport and 49 minutes by foot. To reach the nearest GP surgery was 9 minutes by car, 20 minutes by public transport and 38 minutes by foot.[15] And that presumes that public transport actually exists. In the case of many rural areas bus and train services are simply not available. We are building homes which are going to leave people stranded if they cannot afford to run a car.

But even if we could satisfactorily switch to affordable

electric cars, that wouldn't in itself decarbonise road transport – it would simply mean that cars were running on electricity rather than petrol or diesel. How much carbon that saves rather depends on how the electricity is generated. Moreover, electric vehicles start with a disadvantage because their manufacture involves more greenhouse gas emissions than does a petrol car – thanks largely to the metals which have to be mined for the batteries. According to an analysis by the Argonne National Laboratory in Chicago, making a typical petrol car spews out 5.5 tonnes of carbon dioxide equivalent, while manufacturing a similar electric car is responsible for 8.1 tonnes. As a result, an electric car in the United States must be driven for around 13,500 miles before it can be said to have emitted fewer greenhouse gases than a petrol car. Even in Norway, where much of the country's electricity is produced by hydroelectricity, it would still be necessary to drive 8,400 miles before an electric car was cleaner. Not everyone, though, is so optimistic. A University of Liège study puts the break-even distance for carbon emissions from an electric car versus a petrol car at between 42,000 and 94,000 miles.[16]

An alternative analysis by the International Council on Clean Transportation (ICCT) looks at the expected lifetime emissions from electric versus petrol cars, were both to be kept for 18 years. It finds that the electric car which took to the road in Europe in 2021 will have lifetime emissions between 66 percent and 69 percent lower than those of an equivalent petrol car. This assumes, however, that European countries succeed in decarbonising their electricity supply in line with their declared ambitions – and that the electricity consumed by the battery-powered car becomes cleaner over time.[17]

If that proves to be accurate, going electric would represent a significant cut in carbon emissions from road transport. It isn't, however, getting us to net zero carbon emissions – nor anything like it. To achieve that, it will be necessary to fully decarbonise not only the electricity sector but also the manufacture of steel, plastics and batteries. That is going to be a far harder nut to crack – and we have only 27 years before our self-imposed deadline.

Could we turn to hydrogen rather than batteries as a way of powering cars? There are many in the automotive industry who believe this could end up proving the more practical option. Toyota, which manufactured the first mass-produced hybrid cars but which has fallen behind in the production of pure electric vehicles, has thrown its weight behind hydrogen, marketing a £60,000 medium-sized car called the Mirai. Hyundai, too, has brought a hydrogen car to market. Hydrogen cars have several possible advantages over battery ones: the vehicles currently available can travel around 300 miles on a tankful, about twice as far as base electric models. It takes only five minutes to refill the tank. Moreover, unlike electric cars, performance does not fall away at low temperatures. The heavier and bulkier the vehicle, the greater the distances that a vehicle is required to travel, the more competitive hydrogen is likely to be. There are already hydrogen buses running in the city of Aberdeen, and there is a widespread assumption that lorries, too, are more likely in the future to be powered this way than by battery.

The hydrogen infrastructure, however, lags several years behind that of electric cars. As of December 2021 there were just 14 filling stations in Britain where it was possible to obtain hydrogen. This, of course, could increase – and we would never need to plaster the country with as many hydrogen pumps as we would electrical chargers. But the issue of cost is as acute for hydrogen vehicles as it is for electric cars. At present, hydrogen cars cost around twice as much to buy as petrol versions – and twice as much to run. Could costs come down? You would hope so, but we have already been into the costs of hydrogen production, and the outlook is not great. If we are going to have zero-emission hydrogen vehicles then we have to produce the hydrogen by zero-carbon means – there is no point in using hydrogen as it is produced today, from fossil fuels.

'Blue' hydrogen, manufactured from coal or gas, is always going to be more expensive than the fossil fuels from which it is made. As for 'green' hydrogen, produced via electrolysis of water, it is always going to struggle to be cost-competitive because of the huge energy losses involved. According to an estimate by the Centre for Sustainable Road Freight, once you take into account the losses along the way, the wheels of a hydrogen-powered truck would have at their disposal just 23 percent of the electrical energy that was used to manufacture the hydrogen.[18] Hydrogen power is only really going to be economical if it makes use of energy which we could not otherwise use, such as surplus electricity generated on sunny and windy days when demand is low.

Could we electrify roads, as we electrify railways or tram-lines? If we are going to have electric lorries and buses it is probably the only option, in the absence of some seismic breakthrough in battery technology. A bus or lorry which could pick up power while it was being driven along would not need to spend hours of the day out of service being recharged. Nor would it be necessary to electrify every mile of road – the most likely solution is a combination of electrified main roads combined with batteries to allow vehicles to complete journeys at low speeds on minor roads. Compared with today's electric cars, a vehicle which could charge while travelling would need smaller, lighter batteries – reducing the manufacturing cost considerably.

It is more difficult and expensive to electrify a road compared with a railway for obvious reasons: a train running along tracks is easier to keep in contact with a wire. A road vehicle, by contrast, wanders all over the road. To attempt to electrify roads is not new, however. The first trolleybus ran in Berlin in 1882 – three years before the first car with internal combustion engine took to the roads. Trolleybuses ran in Britain from 1911 to 1972, and elsewhere in the world, 300 trolleybus systems are still operational. Could we extend the idea much more broadly? There are several demonstration projects for electrified highways around the world. Siemens – which was responsible for the Berlin trolleybus in 1882 – has installed overhead electricity cables along the inner lane of a stretch of freeway in Los Angeles. Lorries pick up power, like an electric train, via a pantograph. In this case, it retracts automatically when the driver uses the indicators, to allow the vehicle to overtake and to turn off the road.

The 'eRoad Arlanda', which runs for a few miles between Stockholm airport and a distribution centre, has been in operation since 2012, using a live rail set into the road surface. Vehicles pick up electricity via a rod which dangles from their undersides, and which retracts if they leave the lane to overtake. In contrast to overhead wires, a ground-based system is much easier to adapt for use by cars as well as lorries. A more elegant solution has been installed by an Israeli start-up company, Electreon, in Tel Aviv and in the Swedish island of Gotland, with further projects planned in Germany and Italy. This consists of induction loops set beneath the tarmac to enable the contactless charging of vehicles as they are driven above – 'dynamic wireless charging' or 'wireless power transfer', as it is known. There are obvious advantages to this system over the others in that it allows vehicles to be driven from lane to lane without having to worry about disconnecting from and reconnecting with a wire or rail. The disadvantage of dynamic wireless charging is that you lose a fair slice of the energy that you are trying to transfer to the moving vehicle. To be efficient, it requires a very small air gap between road and vehicle, and for the driver to follow a very close alignment with the hidden coils. Trials of seven such systems around the world have resulted in anything from 10 to 30 percent of the energy being lost in the transfer. And that is under test conditions; it would be a different matter in real-life driving.[19] Static wireless charging, by contrast – where the vehicle is charged while parked over an electronic grid – has been shown to transfer energy at an efficiency between 92 and 97 percent.[20] A 30 percent loss of energy is very significant – equivalent to reducing a petrol car's fuel economy from 45 miles per gallon to 30. There are also safety issues to be considered with strong electromagnetic fields. While trials have shown that the electromagnetic radiation emitted by wireless power transfer systems in cars can be brought within acceptable levels with appropriate engineering of the underside of the vehicle, there is a wide variation in standards accepted between countries.[21]

These are all interesting technologies, some of which might well succeed. But they have two things in common. Firstly, they are still very much at the early development stage. Secondly, if they are to decarbonise all road transport they will require vast investment in infrastructure – both in the apparatus which would need to be installed along the roads and also in the extra-low carbon generating capacity which would be needed to supply enough power to feed the electrified roads. What makes sense to install on densely used urban roads may not make sense on lesser-used roads.

In Britain, the Centre for Sustainable Road Freight has proposed installing overhead wires on 4,700 miles of motorways to feed heavy goods vehicles – a project it claims could be delivered for £19.3 billion private investment by the end of the 2030s. Such a system would cover 65 percent of freight journeys in Britain. Commercial vehicle-owners, it claims, could earn back their investment in electric trucks in 18 months through lower fuel costs (although, as with electric cars, the sums look very different once you make allowance for the inevitability that government is going to dream up new road taxes to replace lost revenue from road fuel). Investors, it claims, could earn back their investment within 15 years.[22]

While that proposal remains on the drawing board, the government has backtracked on a £30 billion scheme to electrify 7,800 miles of railway over the next few years, and now seems to be leaning towards hydrogen trains as a potentially cheaper means of reaching its target of phasing out diesel locomotives by 2040 and decarbonising rail travel. This is where dreams and demonstration projects collide head-on with economic reality. If it is ruled too expensive to undertake simple rail electrification projects – a long-proven technology – what chance that we are going to succeed in building a much more challenging network of electrified roads in time for our self-imposed deadline of going net zero by 2050? To achieve that we would need to start throwing vast sums of money at an electrified road infrastructure in the very near future. The inevitable danger of the unseemly rush is that we end up committing to the wrong technology, paying billions to install, say, overhead wires for use by lorries and buses and then regretting that we didn't opt for a system which was capable of allowing cars, too, to recharge while on the go.

There could have been a better way for road transport – but it has already been undermined by the government. That would have been to embrace hybrid vehicles as a stepping stone to electric ones – or perhaps to a future of cars using a mixture of battery power backed up by synthetic fuels. Hybrids overcome the problem of a lack of range and charging infrastructure. The technology is already there – hybrid cars have been on the roads for over a decade. A lot of hybrid cars, it is true, are token gestures – they have normal-sized petrol or diesel engines, with a few added batteries, the latter of which are only able to power the car for less than 20 miles. But the technology was developing. We were beginning to see 'series' hybrids which were essentially electric cars with a small petrol engine to recharge the batteries for long journeys. Take out the peaks of energy demand when you need to accelerate uphill, and you only need a small engine. In time, those engines could have been run on biofuel or synthetic fuel (of which more in the next chapter). But then the government destroyed the future market for hybrids, and with it all innovation, by announcing that all new sales will be banned by 2035.

Under net zero, unless there is some miracle technological breakthrough, cars will almost certainly become a luxury; we will return to the world as it was before the 1960s, with the wealthy allowed to drive around on pleasantly empty roads, but with everyone else expected to take the bus. Worst of all, the government is not being honest and open about it. And worse still, planning policy continues to assume car-dependency. We are heading for a very large crunch which leaves people isolated in homes from which they will struggle to reach places of work, schools, shops and leisure facilities. That is simply cruel.

11.

Aviation and shipping

IT SAYS SOMETHING ABOUT THE global commitment to eliminate carbon emissions that the world cannot even agree to tax airline fuel. World leaders will preach climate Armageddon at every international summit, and will make grand promises to eliminate all emissions by some future date, yet they cannot manage a simple reform which could help to incentivise the use of more fuel-efficient aircraft. All they need to do is to repeal the 1944 Chicago Convention and the many bilateral and multilateral agreements since which have kept airline fuel tax-free. The EU – seen by many as a leader in taking action against climate change – did discuss removing the tax exemption on aviation fuel back in the mid-1990s, but quickly dropped the matter. The EU has now resurrected proposals for a tax on aviation fuel, but only on that used for internal flights.

When it comes to reducing your country's carbon footprint, aircraft don't even officially count – as aviation and shipping are excluded from the UN's methodology of calculating a nation's emissions. Once you are in the air or on the high seas you can spew out as much carbon as you like and it fails to register on your 'territorial' emissions.

Finally, though, the UK government has given in to pressure and decided that aviation and shipping should, at some point, be included in its legally binding target of achieving net zero by 2050. This produces something of a problem, as aviation is going to be one of the hardest sectors of the economy to decarbonise. Some scientist-activists are brutally honest about what they want to happen. UK FIRES – a collaboration of several UK universities, whose stated purpose is to develop the skills and knowledge 'to address the scientific and technological challenges facing the nation', and which is funded by public money through the Engineering and Physical Sciences Research Council – stated in a report in 2019: 'There are no options for zero-emissions flight in the time available for action, so the industry faces a rapid contraction. Developments in electric flight may be relevant beyond 2050.'[1] In other words, we need to save the planet, so no jetting off on holidays for the next 30 years – although we might, if we are all good, get to fly somewhere on an electric plane sometime after 2050.

The government insists the opposite: that the means will somehow be found to ensure that we will continue to have an aviation industry as we approach 2050 and net zero – and moreover that ordinary people will still be able to take to the air. Clearly, both views cannot be right. So who is right: government or government-funded scientists and technologists? Is it business as usual or planes relegated to museums? Or is the reality likely to fall somewhere in between?

There is no shortage of innovation being employed in trying to decarbonise the aviation industry. And I don't mean the dubious practice of asking passengers whether they would like to pay a small supplement to 'offset' their emissions by planting a tree or something. The spirit of Biggles is still alive. In 2021 several planes took off around the world aimed at pioneering ways towards zero-carbon flight. A six-seater Piper plane converted to run on hydrogen by Californian start-up ZeroAvia took off from Cranfield Airport in Bedfordshire (it later crash-landed, though thankfully without injuries). Rolls-Royce engineered an electric, battery-powered plane, the *Spirit of Innovation*, which took off from a Ministry of Defence aircraft testing site at Boscombe Down in Wiltshire and completed a 10-mile flight, reaching a maximum speed of 390 mph; on another test flight it climbed 3,000 metres in 202 seconds.[2] A microlight aircraft called Ikarus C42 (perhaps not the most comforting name for a test plane) took off from Cotswold Airport in Gloucestershire and completed a short flight powered entirely by synthetic fuel made from hydrogen, itself manufactured from water, and from carbon dioxide captured from the air. Unlike the fabled Icarus, nothing melted; indeed, its government-backed promoters claimed that the plane had been able to run at lower temperatures than a similar plane powered by fossil fuel, and that this could have beneficial effects on long-term engine wear.

On a larger scale, United Airlines flew a Boeing 737 MAX 8 from Chicago to Washington using 500 gallons of ordinary jet fuel in one of its engines and the same quantity of biofuel in the other. For the moment, that is as far as a passenger jet is allowed to experiment with biofuels – regulations prevent using biofuel or synthetic fuel in both engines. But if you can fly 600 miles on one engine powered by biofuel it is a fair guess that you can do it with both engines powered in that way. The principle, at least, of non-fossil-fuel-based airline flight has been established.

But, as always, there are two big hurdles to be overcome: firstly the cost and secondly ensuring that the innovative planes really are zero carbon. According to an analysis by the European Commission biofuel can currently be grown and manufactured at a cost of between €2.26 and €3.25 per litre. Ordinary jet fuel, by contrast, costs just €0.40 to €0.60 to manufacture.[3] Given that fuel typically accounts for between 20 and 30 percent of an airline's overall costs, using biofuel at present would more than double the cost of flying.

Cost, however, is not the only problem with biofuels – there is also the issue of finding enough biomass to create the fuels. The biofuel industry has itself calculated how much land the

United States would need to grow the crops to satisfy its demand for liquid fuels (for all uses, not just aviation). Make them from soybean and you can derive around 40 gallons of fuel per acre per year – which would require 5.6 million square miles' worth of crops. The trouble is that the United States extends to only 3.7 million square miles. Corn produces biofuel more intensively, delivering potentially up to 400 gallons per acre per year, cutting the land required to 560,000 square miles.[4] The United States could find the land, but only just – in 2018, 610,000 square miles were in use for arable production. Sugar cane would bring the demand for land down further again, to 260,000 square miles, but that still takes a huge amount of farmland out of production. It would be a bad outcome if the rich world satisfied its demand for non-fossil fuel at the cost of driving up the price of food for the poor. Indeed, biofuel, in its early years, was blamed for surging food prices.

If those are the figures for the United States, it would be far harder still to satisfy demand for biofuels in Britain, which is already only 60 percent self-sufficient in food. We could import crops, but that would require large areas of plantation to be created elsewhere in the world – in practice almost certainly involving the removal of large areas of forest in South America or Indonesia. Since the first flush of enthusiasm for biofuels in the 2000s, many people have settled on the principle that biofuels are a bad thing when whole crops are dedicated to their production, but can be a good thing if the fuels are made exclusively from chaff and other crop waste. But that greatly reduces the amount of biomass available to be turned into biofuels. The International Energy Agency has set a target that 45 percent of biofuels should be made from wastes and residues. Yet in 2020 only 7 percent of biofuels were made in this way. In the same year just 3 percent of transport fuels used globally were biofuels – which includes the 10 percent ethanol now added to most petrol sold in Britain (fulfilling a target set during the country's EU member-ship, under the Renewable Energy Directive). It shows just what an onerous demand it would place on global agriculture were we to try to power all transport from stuff grown on the land.

Could we grow biofuels in the water? That was a fashion-able suggestion a decade ago, when great claims were made for the potential of algae as a biofuel. But the promise has not yet materialised, largely because of the costs – a UK Parliament study in 2011 estimated the cost of producing algae biofuels at $3 (then £1.90) per litre. By contrast, the cost of a litre of unleaded in early 2022, minus the tax, was around 60 pence per litre. Moreover, the same study questioned whether they even would succeed in cutting carbon emissions. It takes a lot of energy to process algae into biofuels, and there are many other environmental factors to consider. Estimates of the carbon emissions saved by making algae biofuel instead of diesel varied from an 80 percent reduction to a threefold increase – in other words, we could end up paying nearly three times as much money for a fuel which was actually releasing three times as much carbon into the atmosphere.[5]

But what of the other options for fossil fuel-free flight – such as the Ikarus option? What if we made fuel synthetically, directly from hydrogen and carbon dioxide? We would not then have the problem of having to grow crops – we could source hydrogen from water and carbon dioxide directly from the air. But we would have to find a lot of zero-carbon energy to produce the fuel. As with biofuels, the cost implications are huge. According to the German Aerospace Center, to produce synthetic jet fuel at current technology would cost €2.26 per litre – similar, indeed, to the cost of biofuels. Looking ahead to 2050, engineering consultancy Ludwig-Bölkow-Systemtechnik sees the cost of producing the fuels coming down, but reckons that even then they would still cost twice as much as conventional jet fuel does at present.[6] Maybe that doesn't sound too bad, but it is a struggle to work out how we are going to move in the direction of more expensive, non-fossil fuels if the world cannot agree to tax airline fuel. The most obvious way of moving the industry in that direction would be to place a tax on conventional jet fuel in order to subsidise the development of synthetic fuels. If this is not an option, it is hard to see that Britain or any other individual country could move to decarbonise its aviation industry unilaterally.

But then do we need to turn hydrogen into a synthetic fuel when we could use it on its own – either by burning it in jet engines or generating power from fuel cells in order to power propellers? Hydrogen-powered planes, like electric cars, go back further than we might imagine. The US military was experimenting with them in the 1950s, while the Soviets experimented with a hydrogen-powered airliner in the late 1980s. Hydrogen has the attraction of having a very high power-to-weight ratio, but the disadvantage of having a low power-to-volume ratio. Even when cooled and compressed into a liquid at minus 250 degrees Celsius – which creates operational problems of its own – it occupies four times as much space as the equivalent amount of jet fuel containing the same energy. That requires planes to be redesigned in ways that make them a lot less space-efficient and less aerodynamic, too. There is the danger of explosion to consider, while hydrogen also has the unfortunate effect of turning metals more brittle. All this said, Airbus has said that it thinks it will be able to get a large airliner flying on hydrogen by 2035. ZeroAvia reckons on having its first passenger flights in 2023, with 575-mile commercial flights by 2026.[7]

What about the electric option? Rolls-Royce has proved that you can get an electric plane into the air, but there are aeroplanes and there are aeroplanes. What might be practical for a light aircraft flying a few miles is a world away from what is practical for a passenger jet crossing the Atlantic. While a litre of jet fuel weighs 0.75 kg and contains around 35 MJ of energy, a lithium battery capable of delivering the same amount of energy weighs around 50 kg. Given that between 40 and 45 percent of the take-off weight of a long-haul airliner is fuel you can see the difficulty here, but we can have some fun trying to get a battery-powered transatlantic jet into the air. Take a Boeing 777, which has a maximum take-off weight of 350 tonnes. Of this, 145 tonnes will be the airliner itself, another 145 tonnes will be fuel and 60 tonnes will be passengers, luggage and freight. Now let's replace those 145 tonnes of fuel with some batteries capable of providing the same energy (they won't quite do the same job because they won't drive jet engines, only power less efficient propellers, but let's leave this aside). The batteries are going to weigh 9,700 tonnes, meaning that the total weight of the aircraft has increased to just under 10,000 tonnes. That's the weight of the Eiffel Tower. Our Boeing 777 isn't going to be taking off – indeed, it won't even get onto the runway. It will have collapsed at the airport stand.

Battery technology will no doubt improve, but at present we are a couple of orders of magnitude away from having battery-powered planes which could be as light as a fully fuelled jet airliner. And, of course, the jet plane gets lighter as it burns fuel, reducing energy consumption as the journey goes on. Unless you are going to pitch your lithium cells overboard as they discharge their energy, your battery plane is going to be just as heavy when it lands as when it took off. That further limits operations, as a fully fuelled plane tends to be difficult to land at its take-off weight – which is why planes which experience an emergency and need to land shortly after take-off must first try to dump some of their fuel.

Put all this together and could we have an aviation industry in a net zero Britain? We could maybe hop from Scottish island to Scottish island on electric planes. We might be able to fly short-haul routes by hydrogen. If we want to fly longer distances we can manufacture fuel – from hydrogen and carbon dioxide rather than biomass if we want to eat as well as to fly – if we don't mind ticket prices doubling. The trouble is, though, that none of these solutions will really get us to zero emissions – or anything like it. To do that we will first have to eliminate carbon emissions from the steel, aluminium, plastics, rubber tyres and many other components, of which more later.

We have already looked at the costs of producing hydrogen. But even if we did power all our planes by hydrogen it wouldn't be enough to counter the effect of aviation on climate change. Getting to net zero isn't just about carbon emissions – it is about eliminating all greenhouse gases, one of which is water vapour, spewed out by jet airliners in the form of 'contrails'. These constitute a surprisingly high proportion of an aircraft's contribution to the greenhouse effect. On calculations produced by McKinsey & Co. in 2020, flying a jet airliner on synthetic fuels would reduce its greenhouse gas emissions by between 30 and 60 percent. The most effective way of reducing overall emissions from planes, found McKinsey, would be by using propeller planes powered by hydrogen fuel cells, which would cut emissions by between 75 and 90 percent.[8] That might be a useful contribution to cutting greenhouse emissions (as indeed are the incremental gains in fuel efficiency of aircraft over the past half century, something we have hardly noticed), but when you have legally committed yourself to net zero emissions it isn't enough. We will still have to find some other way of mitigating emissions if we want to carry on flying – which adds a lot more expense.

In other words, I would say it is the UK FIRES people who are right and the government which is wrong: if we are determined to reach net zero by 2050 it will pretty well have to involve the end of the airline industry in its current form, with perhaps only small planes still able to fly.

But even if we did succeed in decarbonising aviation in Britain, would the rest of the world follow suit? Much as the academics of UK FIRES might wish it, there is little sign of contraction in the airline industry in China. On the contrary, as UK environmentalists fight the government over a third runway for Heathrow Airport − first proposed in 1946 − China's current five-year plan includes proposals for 29 new airports by 2025,[9] while the Chinese Civil Aviation Administration has floated proposals for a total of 450 airports by 2035, up from 241 at the end of 2020.[10] It is certainly not planning to power the planes using those airports by hydrogen or biofuels. For China, keen to spread its influence around the world, there could be no more delightful prospect than that of Western governments voluntarily shrinking their air links.

Ships do not have to get airborne and so weight is not quite such an issue, but trying to decarbonise them does bring its own challenges. The container ships on which the modern economy has come to rely have to travel for weeks without recourse to fuel and other supplies. That is fine when powered, as they are now, by heavy fuel oil. Could we power them by battery instead? Let's take a Maersk Triple E container ship producing 60 MW of power from its two engines − consuming 1,440 MWh of energy every day at its cruising speed of 16 knots. In ten days at sea it will consume 14,400 MWh of energy. You can obtain that energy from around 1,250 tonnes of oil. Lithium batteries, on the other hand, can store around 200 kWh of energy per tonne, meaning that we are going to need around 72,000 tonnes' worth of batteries to keep the boat going for ten days. That is more than the 55,000 tonnes that the ship weighs when empty. Given that the maximum laden weight of the vessel is 210,000 tonnes you could theoretically fill a container ship with the quantity of batteries required for ten days at sea, but only at the cost of having to leave behind on the dockside about half your cargo.

It is tempting to think that a ship crossing the tropics might be able to generate a fair proportion of its own energy from the sun. But even if we could pack the 2.4-hectare deck solidly with solar panels, and the sun always shone, that would provide only around 2.5 MW of power – less than a twentieth of the power required to keep the ship moving. Could we go back to wind power, which, after all, is how we powered ocean-going ships for centuries? There are at least a hundred companies and organisations which claim to be developing modern wind-powered or wind-assisted vessels. Among the most advanced is Swedish company Wallenius, which hopes to have two 32,000-tonne ocean-going ships, capable of carrying 7,000 cars across the Atlantic at a speed of 10 knots and powered by retractable steel 'sails', operational by 2027.

We can wish this technology well, but for the moment it is no more than a concept – which I have to say bears a remarkable resemblance to the drawings which used to pop up in popular science magazines in the 1970s, when the shipping industry last dabbled with the idea of a return to wind power. For the moment, if you really want your goods delivered by sea without fossil fuels your best hope is via a Dutch company called Fair Transport which has been operating a 1940s schooner, the *Tres Hombres*, across the Atlantic for the past decade. The figures demonstrate just how far we have come since the age of sail: the 105-foot ship requires a crew of seven and can carry 35 tonnes of cargo.[11] You can fit more into two shipping containers. A Maersk Triple E vessel, by contrast, can carry 18,000 such containers – with the aid of a crew of 13. Sail power might be charming and clean, and provide a boutique service for the eco-conscious – but for the moment it is no basis for a global freight industry in a modern industrial economy. Some might argue that is a good thing if container ships were to disappear, that we should learn to consume goods produced more locally. But those people are not merely arguing for the mitigation of climate impacts from carbon emissions; they are advocating a return to pre-industrial existence – and the poverty which that would entail.

The shipping industry itself is looking into a future of biofuels and manufactured fuels in the form of methanol and ammonia. According to the International Renewable Energy Agency (IRENA), it is the latter that we should expect to be powering large ships by 2050. Ammonia, though, is toxic and difficult to handle. In order to be stored as a liquid it must be kept at either minus 34 degrees Celsius or at high pressures. Per MWh, a tankful of ammonia will weigh three times as much and occupy three times as much space as a tankful of oil. These are all problems which can be overcome – at a cost. But there is also the cost of the fuel itself. There are no ammonia wells that we can tap into; it will have to be manufactured from hydrogen, which, if it is going to be carbon neutral, will have to be made via energy-hungry electrolysis of water. Using current technology 1 MWh worth of ammonia fuel can be manufactured for between $150 and $220. Even assuming improvements in technology (which can't be taken for granted), IRENA expects it in 2050 still to cost between $67 and $114 for every MWh worth of ammonia fuel. In 2019, by contrast, shipping lines paid between $19 and $41 for the equivalent quantity of oil.[12] To imagine that ammonia can ever compete with fossil fuels is wishful thinking: as with any synthetic fuel, you are always going to lose a hefty slice of energy during the manufacturing process. In the case of ammonia there is a double helping of losses – the first in the production of hydrogen from water and the second in the production of ammonia from hydrogen.

It is hard to see how depriving the shipping industry of

fossil fuels is going to do anything other than add significantly to the expense of transporting goods around the world. And, of course, opting for zero-carbon fuel doesn't get close to decarbonising the shipping industry. There is also the small matter of the steel which goes into the manufacture of ships – around 50,000 tonnes of it into each of the largest vessels – plus making the containers. That is another carbon-intensive industry whose decarbonisation we have yet to grapple with.

12.

Industry

WHEN DOCUMENTS ON NET ZERO are illustrated with images of wind turbines and solar panels we are invited to think that is more or less where it begins and ends – with renewable energy. When we look at a wind turbine, however, we are also looking at one of the most carbon-intensive industries there is. Yet who really sees the steel – a commodity which is itself responsible for between 7 and 11 percent of total greenhouse gas emissions (according to various estimates)? Still less do we see the concrete into which the turbine's foundations are set – the product of a cement industry which accounts for a further 7 percent of global emissions. Between them, steel and cement are responsible for around one in every six tonnes of CO_2 emissions. Moreover, it is far from easy to see how either of these industries can be fully decarbonised at reasonable cost without some ground-breaking technology which has yet to be invented.

Steel-making and cement-making are both energy-intensive, but that is not the real problem. Both involve chemical processes which themselves emit large quantities of carbon dioxide – so-called 'process emissions'. In order to make steel from iron ore it is first necessary to 'reduce' the iron ore – which means removing the oxygen from iron oxides in order to leave the iron behind, usually achieved by heating the oxides in the presence of coke. The carbon in the coke reacts with the oxygen in the iron oxides to produce carbon dioxide, which is then released into the air. Traditionally, and as still is the case of just over 70 percent of the world's steel-making, this process is undertaken in blast furnaces, using large quantities of coking coal as the reducing agent. Steel plants also use large quantities of electricity, much of it generated by fossil fuels, but even if they could use 100 percent zero-carbon, renewable energy it would reduce their carbon emissions by less than 10 percent – from 2.23 tonnes of carbon dioxide for every tonne of steel produced to 2.06 tonnes of carbon dioxide.[1] That is how important process emissions are in steel-making.

We can clean up the steel industry to some extent, but it won't come cheap. Coking coal is not the only reducing agent that we could be using – we could use hydrogen, which, if it is 'green' hydrogen manufactured from electrolysis of water using renewable energy, could in theory allow steel-making to be zero carbon. The most straightforward way to reduce emissions would be to replace some of the coking coal used in blast furnaces with hydrogen. Indeed, this has already been done in a number of plants and has succeeded in reducing carbon emissions by around a fifth. For technical reasons, however, it is not possible to replace all the coking coal with hydrogen. If we want to get the steel industry to anything approaching zero carbon we will have to look to a wholly different process, via an electric arc furnace, combined with direct reduction of iron ore.

Just under a third of world steel already is made in electric arc furnaces – but most of that – 24 percent of global steel production – involves using scrap steel as a raw material. That is fine – and British steel plants could certainly be using more scrap steel, most of which is currently exported. But a growing global economy cannot live on recycled steel alone. What an electric arc furnace cannot do is produce steel directly from iron ore. First, the iron ore must be turned into a material known as 'sponge iron' through a process called direct reduction. This is an established procedure used in around 5 percent of global steel-making, most often using either coal or natural gas as a reducing agent. But demonstration plants have shown that it can also be carried out wholly using hydrogen. At the moment most of that hydrogen is produced using fossil fuels, but it is perfectly technically possible to use green hydrogen.

By this means, steel manufacturers ArcelorMittal and SSAB are individually planning to produce what they claim will be the world's first zero-carbon steel to be produced at volume. ArcelorMittal – with an undisclosed level of support from the Spanish government – is building a plant spread across two sites in Bilbao and Gijón in northern Spain scheduled to start producing zero-carbon steel in 2025, using electricity from a solar farm. Swedish-based SSAB has already produced small quantities of zero-carbon steel but plans to produce it at volume in 2026.

There is, needless to say, a cost penalty. According to analysis by Columbia University, to produce zero-carbon steel using green hydrogen with current technology would add around $350 to the cost of producing each tonne of steel – nearly doubling the price of the finished product.[2] That is conjecture: no one has yet built and operated a commercial-scale hydrogen steel plant, and so we cannot yet know what problems and costs might arise. But what about the cost of supplying a zero-carbon steel plant with electricity? An electric arc furnace is a voracious consumer of power, requiring over 900 kWh of electricity to produce each tonne of steel. Moreover, steel plants need to operate at continuously high temperatures, so are difficult to run with intermittent solar and wind power alone. Add in the cost of renewable electricity, and the need to store it so that it is there to be used when the sun isn't shining and the wind isn't blowing, and the cost of your zero-carbon steel is going to rise a lot further.

It is hard enough for European steel plants to compete with Chinese ones at present. Zero-carbon steel is not going to be a competitive commodity on world markets unless the cost of green hydrogen and the cost of renewable energy and storage both fall dramatically. It is only going to be able to compete in markets where it is heavily subsidised, or where traditional, carbon-intensive producers are hit with high carbon taxes and where high carbon tariffs are imposed to keep out steel produced by more carbon-intensive methods in places such as China – a 'carbon border tax'. But if we protect the embryonic green steel industry with taxes, levies and import tariffs, that drives up the cost of steel for manufacturers of other goods, making their products less competitive. In turn, we would then have to use even more taxes and tariffs in order to penalise imported goods made from non-green steel.

That is one reason why neither the UK nor the EU have yet been able to agree on the imposition of a carbon border tax. In November 2021 UK environment secretary George Eustice suggested that Britain might eventually need a carbon border tax, but the idea has gone no further.[3] The EU proposed a Carbon Border Adjustment Mechanism in July 2021, but a year later it remained bogged down in the European Parliament.

Perversely, the quickest route for Britain to eliminate carbon emissions from steel-making would be to let the domestic steel industry go to the wall and import the metal instead. Never mind replacing steel plants with expensive hydrogen plants and electric arc furnaces – closing down steel plants would, at a stroke, reduce to zero the contribution of steel to Britain's carbon emissions. Why? Because, as we have already discussed, emissions only count as emissions for the sake of Britain's net zero target if they are physically spewed out within the bounds of the country. Import steel from abroad – which in practice is most likely to mean China, which accounted for 56 percent of global steel-making in 2019 – and you send those emissions overseas. It is a case of out of sight, out of mind.

But it won't help the planet. China's two biggest steel-makers, HBIS and Baowu, have both announced projects to experiment with plants using hydrogen, but for the moment and long into the future steel-making in China is, and will remain, a far dirtier process than in the UK or the rest of Europe. Chinese steel-making is the world's single most polluting industry, responsible alone for nearly 4 percent of all global greenhouse gas emissions. In China, 90 percent of steel-making (compared with a global average of 70 percent) is made in blast furnaces, using coking coal. As for the electricity used in steel-making plants, 56 percent of it comes from coal.[4]

As for steel, so for cement. Cement-making is an extremely energy intensive business, requiring high kiln temperatures – which in most cases are obtained by burning fossil fuels. But that isn't the biggest problem. Two thirds of the emissions from a cement kiln emanate not from burning fuel but from the chemical process of turning limestone into clinker. This requires carbon to be removed from the limestone, generating large quantities of carbon dioxide as a by-product. For every tonne of cement produced, 600 kg of carbon dioxide is exhausted to the air.

The UK cement industry can boast of having reduced its carbon emissions in recent decades, which have fallen by 52 percent between 1990 and 2015. But half of that is down to the country producing less cement. Per tonne, emissions have fallen by 27 percent according to the Department for Business, Energy and Industrial Strategy.[5] Even this, though, is questionable, given that it has been achieved in part by heating kilns by burning biomass and industrial waste. This might be regarded as a zero-carbon activity in the miracle world of government carbon-accounting, which counts burning waste as zero-carbon, but it is obvious that the practice does indeed release large quantities of carbon dioxide. Moreover, there is only so much biomass and industrial waste to go around – and there is stern competition for it from the electricity generating business. Another part of the fall in cement industry emissions is down to the use of other materials to bulk up clinker – namely pulverised fuel ash from the boilers of coal-fired power stations and slag from steel blast furnaces. It is not hard to see the problem here – coal-fired power stations will be gone by 2024 and we are also trying to switch away from producing steel in blast furnaces. With them will go the materials which have been used to date to reduce emissions from cement.

It is possible that the cement industry might be able to reduce carbon emissions by heating its kilns with green electricity – using microwaves has been suggested, although this technology has yet to make it out of the laboratory. As for the process emissions – those derived from turning limestone into clinker – there is as yet only one option for trying to decarbonise those: by capturing the carbon dioxide in the chimney of cement works and either pumping it underground or turning it into something solid. This is a technology which is still to be fully commercialised, so it is hard to put a price on it, but it certainly won't come cheap. According to estimates by equity research group Redburn, in a note advising its clients to sell the shares of European cement producers, installing carbon capture and storage (CCS) will push up the price of producing cement by 61 percent.[6] We will deal with carbon capture more in the following chapter.

As with steel, any unilateral attempt to force these costs on European producers will drive up prices, render their products uncompetitive and force us to import cement instead. That ought to be seen as an economic disaster and counterproductive in terms of cutting greenhouse gas emissions, but there is a serious danger that it could end up being celebrated as a triumph – as the emissions from cement consumed in Britain would then be off our national carbon balance sheet.

It is a similar story throughout many industries: solutions to reduce greenhouse gas emissions will add significant extra costs – and won't, on their own, get us to net zero carbon emissions. Plastics? Quite rightly, there has been a strong regulatory move against single-use plastics, such as shopping bags and food packaging, in recent years. A 5-pence surcharge on bags introduced in England in 2015 succeeded in reducing use of bags by 95 percent. That means, hopefully, less plastic pollution making it into rivers, oceans and the environment in general. Where plastic bags are still used they tend now to be more commonly of the biodegradable kind, and so even if they do end up in the environment they should gently rot away.

But it would be foolish to think that a success with reducing usage of plastic bags means that plastics – and the carbon emissions associated with them – are on their way out. Without moving an inch from my desk I could list the following items as including significant quantities of plastic, none of which can easily be replaced with other materials: computer, printer, router, telephone, spectacles, pens, cars, gutters, buckets, wheelie bins… Plastics are in many ways miracle materials which have allowed mass-production of items which were once expensive luxuries. They are indispensable for our standard of living, and are vital in many cases for safety, too. Imagine trying to build an electrical network and appliances without plastics as insulators. The generally negative view towards plastics in Britain changed overnight in the spring of 2020 when we found ourselves fighting the Covid-19 pandemic – and we suddenly realised we had a shortage of personal protective equipment (PPE), vast amounts of which had to be imported for want of production facilities in Britain. It is hard to imagine modern medicine without plastics – nor indeed food production, vehicle production and many other industries.

Notionally, we can produce plastics with far fewer carbon emissions. We don't have to make them from crude oil. Indeed, bioplastics, made from plant materials, have been around for a century and a half and predate the production of plastics made from oil. But there are reasons why at present bioplastics represent less than 1 percent of global plastics production: even where they are suitable, they involve significant extra expense. A US study from 2017 found that bioethylene made from corn cost at least twice as much as the same material made from fossil fuels – between $1,780 and $2,930 per tonne for bioethylene and between $770 and $1,430 for its fossil fuel-produced cousin. That doesn't sound so bad – if you are constructing, say, a car or a computer, the cost of the plastic isn't a huge proportion of the value of the end product. But here's the thing: using bioplastics won't fully decarbonise the plastic industry, or anything like it. Indeed, the same study found that corn-based polymers reduce the carbon footprint of plastic production by only 25 percent – once you have taken into account the emissions involved in growing the corn.[7] The study came to the conclusion that if the plastics industry wants to reduce greenhouse gas emissions quickly, it should start with using renewable energy for the manufacturing process – whether you use corn or crude oil as your feedstock is of lesser importance, contrary to intuition.

If you want to reduce Britain's emissions from the plastics industry to zero, on the other hand, there is a far quicker method still: close down the remaining factories in Britain and import it all. As previously discussed, the way we count carbon emissions – on a purely territorial basis, excluding those imbedded in imports – mitigates against innovation and in favour of simply closing down UK industry. The warnings are there. In October 2022, German plastics manufacturer and industrials giant BASF announced that it was permanently downsizing operations in Europe due to high energy costs – while investing in a new £10 billion factory in China.[8]

The same is true of fertiliser. Next time the government boasts of trimming a few more percent off Britain's territorial emissions it will be thanks in part to CF Fertilisers closing down its ammonia plant near Chester in 2022 – one of two factories in Britain where it produced the gas for use in fertilisers. As far as carbon-accounting purposes were concerned the closure was a triumph. The Haber–Bosch process by which ammonia is made generates vast quantities of CO_2 as a by-product – and is responsible for 1 percent of global carbon emissions.[9] If the purpose of the government's carbon levy was to drive away such an important source of carbon emissions, it has succeeded – high environmental costs are one of the reasons cited by the owners of the plant for its closure. But it is not going to achieve anything for the planet. It will merely mean more fertiliser having to be imported. Ironically, it could also lead to a shortage of carbon dioxide needed by the food industry, for everything from making beer and stunning animals to preserving salads. Already, the government has had to step in to try to save the company's other plant on Teesside for fear of a repeat of carbon dioxide shortages. The use of carbon levies means approaching the problem the wrong way around: they are pushing heavy industry abroad while doing nothing to promote innovation. What we really should be doing is funding research into ways of cleaning up ammonia production, to reduce unwanted emissions of carbon dioxide, not simply shifting the industry's emissions off the national balance sheet.

Britain is already a heavily deindustrialised country. Fewer factories and chimneys mean less pollution close to home, but the loss of industry has come at a cost: it has made us more dependent on imports, exposing us more to interruptions in global supply chains, as we found throughout the Covid-19 pandemic and the Ukraine war. Offshoring our emissions is nothing to be celebrated, and will do nothing to cut global carbon emissions – even if it allows government ministers to boast of creeping ever closer to their target of reaching net zero.

13.

Capturing carbon

THERE IS A 'NET' IN net zero for a reason. As we have just seen, there are areas of the economy which, on technology which exists now or is likely to exist in the near future, it simply will not be possible fully to decarbonise. Hence the concept of net zero offers an escape route; if we can remove greenhouse gases from the atmosphere then we could continue to burn some fossil fuels – perhaps a lot of fossil fuels – and not worry about the emissions. Carbon capture is a kind of atonement for environmental sins.

But how to suck carbon dioxide out of the atmosphere? There are a number of ways in which this could potentially be done. Most simply of all is a carbon-consuming device known as a tree. While they are growing, trees consume very large quantities of carbon dioxide; it is, after all, their food.

The government has big plans for tree-planting. Its Net Zero Strategy sees 30,000 hectares' worth of them being planted every year across the UK by 2025, with at least 7,500 of them in England. The National Audit Office (NAO) is not convinced it has put enough thought into how it hopes to achieve this unprecedented level of tree-planting, and points out that the government is already falling behind. In 2021/22, it calculated, 2,577 hectares of trees would have had to be planted for the government to be on a trajectory to reach its 2025 target. However, the total for the year looks like coming in at between 1,400 and 1,900 hectares.[1]

But even the trees which have been planted have caused enough trouble, making it even more difficult for farmers to find suitable land and thereby reducing Britain's self-sufficiency in food – something which has already fallen from 78 percent in the mid-1980s to 60 percent today. Ian O'Connor, a tenant farmer in Carmarthenshire, West Wales, thought he had secured the future of his sheep-farming business when he had an offer accepted on 270 acres of land. Then he was gazumped by a Guernsey-based company which wanted the land on which to plant trees, partly for forestry but also in order to claim carbon credits – payments for offsetting carbon emissions elsewhere in the economy.[2]

There are several objections to the practice of trying to reach net zero by covering Britain with trees. Making the country more reliant on imported food itself threatens to undermine efforts to achieve carbon neutrality. If we end up transporting meat or arable crops from the other side of the world in order to make up for food that was previously grown in Britain, that will itself involve a rise in emissions. The government does not seem to have taken this into account. Why not? We come back to the same issue as discussed in the previous chapter with industrial products. Imported goods do not count towards Britain's territorial greenhouse gas emissions – the system of accounting which is used to determine carbon neutrality. Therefore, you can create the illusion of cutting emissions by taking UK land out of agricultural production and planting it with trees, but in reality you will have achieved nothing for the planet – especially if land in other countries ends up being cleared of forestry in order to grow food for British consumers.

Planting large areas of fast-growing conifer forests goes back on decades of conservation work. Until recently, the mass-planting of non-native conifers in the early to mid-20th century had come to be seen as an ecological disaster, reducing biodiversity. Instead, the UK forestry industry was moving more towards planting native broadleaf woodlands. But the carbon offsets industry doesn't much like broadleaf trees because they are slower-growing and thus take longer to sequestrate carbon from the atmosphere. Indeed, the Carmarthenshire scheme is planned to consist of only 23 percent native broadleaf woodland, the rest being conifers.

But can we really count the planting of trees as permanently removing carbon dioxide from the atmosphere? A tree will absorb CO_2 while it is growing, but eventually, after a hundred years or so, it will die, rot and re-release the gas to the atmosphere. To effect a permanent removal of carbon dioxide we would need to do something with the wood to prevent it from rotting, such as burying it in anaerobic conditions, or using it in the construction industry, or turning it into biochar – a stable form of carbon which could be spread over agricultural land. A medieval half-timbered building, which contains quantities of carbon dioxide which were extracted from the air several centuries ago, can be counted as a long-term form of carbon-removal. A tree which dies and rots after a century is another matter.

Alternatively, we can assume that a tree, when it eventually dies, will be replaced by another growing tree – and thus count the creation of woodland as involving a one-off chunk of carbon removed from the atmosphere. But how much carbon could we remove by increasing the forest coverage of Britain? A 2018 report by the Royal Society and Royal Academy of Engineering provides some sort of answer. In order to reach net zero by 2050, it calculates, we will need to remove 130 Mt of CO_2 from the air in that year and every subsequent year.[3] This is to compensate for the remaining emissions from industries which will be very hard to decarbonise, such as steel and cement.

To remove a tonne of carbon dioxide from the atmosphere

through the planting of forestry, the report asserts, costs about $30. Given that a transatlantic jet flight releases approximately a tonne of CO_2 per passenger,[4] we could think of this as a reasonable tax on flying. However, we can't just carry on planting trees ad infinitum; we need land, which is in finite supply. But how much land? The Royal Society report quotes research into the carbon removal achieved by planting former mining land with trees. Over the course of 100 years, it calculated, each hectare was able to sequestrate up to 10 tonnes of CO_2 per year. To lock up the 130 million tonnes of CO_2 which will be required to reach net zero we would thus need 13 million hectares of land. That is just over half the 24-million-hectare land surface area of the United Kingdom. At present, the Royal Society puts UK coverage of conifer woodland at 5.1 percent, broad-leafed woodland at 2.2 percent and shrubland at 1.4 percent, although Forest Research – a national statistic – puts the overall UK coverage of woodland markedly higher, at 13 percent.

That might feasibly keep us carbon neutral for the next century, but beyond that? If we wanted to remain net zero we would have to keep on creating new woodland, ad infinitum. Within two centuries we would entirely run out of land in Britain on which to plant new trees. Beyond that timescale we really would have to find some way of keeping carbon locked up in wood for the long term. What about the biochar option, locking up carbon in a stable form by treating wood from felled trees to a process known as pyrolysis, which means burning in a low-oxygen environment? As ever, there is a cost involved – and a large one, too. We don't really know at the moment what it would cost to produce the large quantities of biochar which would be needed to remove significant amounts of carbon from the atmosphere, but one learned estimate quoted by the American University in Washington DC puts the cost at between $30 and $120 per tonne of carbon dioxide removed, and another estimates the cost at between \$18 and \$166 per tonne.[5] That would put the cost of removing the 326 Mt of carbon dioxide emitted in Britain in 2020 at between \$5.9 billion and \$54 billion. The lowest of those figures might sound a bargain, but it doesn't include the land use cost of taking vast tracts of Britain out of agricultural production. The other problem is the time it takes to grow the trees. As previously mentioned, it takes 100 years for each hectare of woodland to soak up its full potential of carbon dioxide. Our 2050 deadline for reaching net carbon emissions will have long been and gone by then. Biochar is only an option for countering carbon emissions on a much longer timescale.

Could we reduce the effective cost of producing biochar by doing something useful with it? There are claims that spreading it on farm land can increase the yield of beetroot (although it proved unprofitable in the case of potatoes).[6] But the world only needs so much beetroot. There are other experiments using it as insulation for building and in the water purification business, but at present we can't really view the production of biochar as anything other than an expensive way (in terms of both money and land use) of removing carbon dioxide from the atmosphere.

But even if we did go ahead with all this planting – and severely shrink UK agriculture in the process – could we really be sure that we were locking up net amounts of carbon? It rather depends on what sort of land we are turning over to forestry. If we end up draining peat and bog in order to plant trees – as was done in large areas of the Flow Country in Caithness and Sutherland, northern Scotland, in the 1970s and 80s and is now recognised as an ecological disaster – we could end up releasing more carbon from the drained soils than we succeed in locking up in the trees. That was the conclusion of a 2020 study by the University of Stirling into carbon emissions from several blocks of peatland which have been planted with forestry.[7]

We would have to be careful, too, about planting trees in upland moorland areas which currently spend large parts of the year covered with snow. Replacing snow-covered areas with trees can also promote the warming of the planet by increasing what is known as the 'albedo' – or reflectivity – of the Earth's surface. Snow reflects incoming solar radiation very well. Turn it into green forest, on the other hand, and it will absorb much more solar radiation, converting it to heat.

If we can't plant trees on the 9.4 percent of the UK land-mass that is currently peat bog or the 7.5 percent that is moorland, that means our carbon-sequestrating forestry will have to eat up even more productive farmland. If we want to maximise the sequestration of carbon per hectare we might look less to cover Britain with trees than to cover much more of it with blanket bog. The 1,500 square miles of bog in the Flow Country are estimated to have sequestrated 400 Mt of carbon, more than twice as much as held in all Britain's trees.[8] But creating bog doesn't happen overnight – it has taken 10,000 years since the end of the last ice age for the Scottish bogs to accumulate up to 10 metres of peat. That is not going to help us meet our 2050 net zero commitment.

Creating new woodlands and bogs is good from an ecological perspective, and creates places which are popular with people for the purposes of leisure – or at least they are when they involve public access and taxpayers' money is not simply thrown at landowners to create their own private nature reserves. But land management on its own is not going to achieve the negative emissions we need to get us to net zero by 2050 nor anything like it. We simply don't have enough land.

What about removing carbon dioxide from the atmosphere by industrial processes instead? Such technology exists, and on a fairly large scale, too. Carbon capture involves using solvents which like to bind to carbon dioxide molecules and so help to remove them from chimney gases and prevent them being exhausted into the atmosphere. The first Carbon Capture, Utilisation and Storage (CCUS) plant was opened in Val Verde, Texas, in 1972, and continues to capture 0.5 Mt of carbon dioxide out of the air every year. Since then, a further 20 CCUS plants have come into operation around the world. Between them they have the capacity to capture up to 40 Mt of carbon dioxide every year. To put that into context, Britain in 2020 emitted 326 Mt of carbon dioxide. Add on other greenhouse gases and it came to a total of 414 Mt of carbon dioxide equivalent.[9] From a global perspective, existing CCUS plants are capable of capturing around one thousandth of current global emissions.

Yet few of these plants were actually designed to sequestrate carbon dioxide from the air. Rather they were set up either to produce carbon dioxide for industrial processes – or, as in the case of the Val Verde plant, to pump carbon dioxide into underground aquifers in order to help push and squeeze out more oil. They are unashamedly a part of the fossil fuel business. The fact that they removed some carbon dioxide from the atmosphere was a by-product of their main function.

That doesn't mean, however, that the technology cannot be used purposefully to remove carbon dioxide from the atmosphere and store it underground where – hopefully – it will remain forever after. Indeed, the technology has been a big part of decarbonisation plans for the past decade and a half. In 2009 the International Energy Agency (IEA) set a target for the world to build 100 large-scale CCUS plants by 2020, preventing a total of 300 Mt of carbon dioxide from being released into the air. In the event, just 15 have been added, sequestrating just 13 percent of the IEA's target.[10]

Why have more not been built? Because CCUS is fantastically

expensive. The Petra Nova coal-fired power station completed in Texas in 2017 is kitted out with CCUS technology which removes 1.4 Mt of carbon dioxide each year from the station's exhaust gases. It is a demonstration project for a technology which could allow countries to carry on burning coal and cut carbon emissions at the same time. But each of those tonnes of carbon dioxide captured by the Petra Nova plant cost $65 to remove from exhaust gases.[11] Let's think big for a minute and imagine covering Britain with CCUS plants. At this rate it would theoretically cost $29 billion to remove the 447.9 million tonnes of carbon dioxide equivalent emitted in Britain in 2019. The designers of the Petra Nova plant claim that were they to build a similar plant now they could bring down the cost to $45 per tonne – which would mean the theoretical cost of removing Britain's annual carbon emissions down to $20 billion. But this is only theoretical – based on the assumption that all carbon emissions are from large chimneys, but of course they are not. In practice, it costs much less to capture carbon from a carbon-dioxide-rich atmosphere like the exhaust gases of a power station than it does to capture it from diffuse sources like car exhausts and gas boilers. It is possible to capture carbon dioxide from plain air, as opposed to chimney smoke – a process known as direct air capture – but this is vastly more difficult and expensive because the concentration of CO_2 is far, far less. While the exhaust gases from a gas-fired power station are made up of 8–10 percent CO_2 and those from a coal-fired power station 12 percent, carbon dioxide makes up only 0.04 percent of normal air. This takes the technology into a different cost league still – to between $130–$340 per tonne, according to the IEA.[12] If you wanted to tackle Britain's carbon emissions in this way you would be looking at a cost of upwards of $58 billion a year.

Except you would struggle to find sufficient space to store the carbon dioxide. Most of the CCUS plants proposed in

Britain, such as that being developed at Drax power station in North Yorkshire, involve carbon dioxide being pressurised into a liquid and then pumped out to chambers beneath the North Sea – voids from which oil and gas has previously been extracted. But only a certain amount of such space exists. The British Geological Survey has identified a possible 500 sites beneath the North Sea capable of storing 70 billion tonnes of carbon dioxide – which would be enough to store 165 years' worth of UK emissions at 2021 levels.[13] But we don't really know how much of this would be suitable. One of the most studied formations, the Captain Sandstone beneath the Moray Firth, was reported in 2012 to have space to store around five years' worth of UK emissions.[14] However, subsequent analysis suggested that it was riddled with fissures, making it unsuitable.[15]

Can we rely on stored carbon dioxide remaining underground? There is little point in the exercise if we can't be sure that it won't leak out through fissures and old wells. Moreover, escaping CO_2 can be a deadly hazard, as was demonstrated in 1986 when several hundred thousand tonnes of naturally occurring carbon dioxide deposits in Lake Nyos in Cameroon bubbled to the surface. Being more dense than air, the invisible clouds of carbon dioxide settled close to the ground in local villages, killing 1,700 people. Of six underground carbon dioxide storage sites which have been monitored, no leakage has yet been traced,[16] but we don't really know the long-term risks. All we have is attempts to model the behaviour of carbon dioxide underground. We will need to have better data than that to be sure we are not wasting our time before we commit to CCUS on a massive scale.

Owners of coal and gas plants already have some sort of incentive to equip plants with CCUS. By doing so they could avoid high carbon taxes. Yet in spite of this, economics does not currently favour the practice. According to the IEA the median levelised cost of producing electricity from gas-powered stations in 2020, assuming carbon taxes at $30 per tonne of carbon dioxide, was $71 per MWh. Add CCUS to the plant, and you can skip paying the carbon taxes, yet even so the cost rises to $91 per MWh. The corresponding figures for coal plants are $88 without CCUS and $119 with CCUS.[17] In other words, it is still cheaper to run your fossil fuel plant without CCUS and simply cough up the tax.

But what if, instead of just pumping it underground to be stored forever after, we could make something useful, something of value from the captured carbon? Could that change the economics? It is potentially possible to do this – and in a way that could both be safer and perhaps more reliable than pumping carbon dioxide into underground reservoirs in liquid form. Some minerals, given the chance, will combine with and absorb carbon dioxide to form carbonate materials which could be of use to the construction industry. There are various technologies in development, such as using mineral slags from iron and steel production to react with carbon dioxide and produce construction materials. The same is being attempted using crushed rocks such as basalt and gabbro. Alternatively, fresh concrete could be injected with carbon dioxide. Portland cement could potentially absorb half its weight in carbon dioxide. According to the National Academies of Sciences, Engineering and Medicine in the United States, global manufacture of cement or other building materials has the potential to absorb one gigatonne of carbon dioxide a year – one thirtieth of global carbon emissions in 2020.[18] But here's the thing: cement production itself accounts for around 7 percent of global carbon emissions. So if, say, you somehow managed to use all the world's concrete production to sequestrate CO_2 you wouldn't even succeed in offsetting the carbon emitted from the production of the cement itself. That might well be a good thing, but it does not provide the basis for disposing of carbon more generally.

Capturing carbon is not an easy business, as demonstration projects have been finding. It is relatively efficient when you start with gas that is very rich in carbon dioxide, such as that flowing up an industrial chimney. It is harder and more expensive to capture carbon dioxide when it is present at much lower concentrations. Moreover, the presence of water vapour can hinder the process, and in many cases the absorption of carbon dioxide is very slow.

The IEA puts the costs of removing a tonne of carbon dioxide from the air by various methods, using current technology:

Biomass plant equipped with CCUS	$15–85
Direct air capture and storage	$135–340
Enhanced weathering of minerals	$50–200
Land management and biochar	$30–120
Forestation	$5–50[19]

There is great potential in many of these technologies, and it is right they be investigated and developed. But as things stand, it is punitively expensive to use CCUS technologies to remove large quantities of carbon dioxide from the air. Moreover, we cannot as yet always trust captured carbon to remain captured, without which the whole business is pointless. The one method of carbon sequestration which does look affordable – and safe – is forestation. But that quickly runs into issues of land use. So, too, does biomass-burning. The implications have simply not been thought through. It will be possible for large countries with relatively low population densities to claim carbon neutrality through tree-planting. Indeed, as we have already seen, Russia's entire net zero strategy revolves around letting forestry take the strain.

But for a small, densely populated country like Britain, trying to use trees to help us reach net zero would severely impact our ability to produce food. For Britain and many other Western European countries the only practical form of carbon sequestration practical in the long term is CCUS – which is vastly more expensive and which has yet to be proved on a commercial scale. We are condemning ourselves to huge costs on consumers and taxpayers, while land-rich countries could claim to have reached net zero with no such costs.

14.

Agriculture

WHO ARE THE WORST 'CLIMATE CRIMINALS' (as activists would put it)? Oil company executives? Celebrities who preach on climate change and then go off and fly by private jet between their mansions? There is another possible candidate for the dishonour – the creatures contentedly chewing the cud in a field near you.

In common with other ruminants such as sheep and deer, cattle pre-digest their food by allowing it to ferment – a process which produces large quantities of methane which get belched and farted into the atmosphere. A cow with a healthy appetite will produce around 100 kg of methane every year. Given that methane is estimated to have 23 times as powerful a greenhouse effect as carbon dioxide, this translates to 2,300 kg of carbon dioxide equivalent – about one quarter of the carbon emissions attributed annually to each human inhabitant of Britain. Hence farting and belching cattle have become the bogeymen – or bogey creatures – of agriculture. Many environmental organisations, including the government's Climate Change Committee, have demanded that the numbers of cattle and other farm animals be seriously reduced; that we all commit to eating less beef and dairy products – or preferably none at all – for the sake of the climate. The government has not yet gone as far as New Zealand, which in June 2022 announced its intention of placing the world's first tax on belching cattle, but it is perhaps only a matter of time.

There is something rather unfair about trying to blame the livestock industry for greenhouse gas emissions. There were, after all, large numbers of ruminants living on Earth long before humans started burning fossil fuels – they were part of a natural carbon cycle. You might as well rail against animals for breathing. Unlike carbon dioxide, methane in the atmosphere breaks down after around a decade – although it does still leave carbon dioxide behind. There must always have been large quantities of methane swirling around in the atmosphere from the front and rear ends of ruminating beasts. Even in the modern United States with its massive appetite for burgers and milk shakes, the number of cattle – 95 million – is not so very much greater that the 60 million bison which are estimated to have lived there before European settlement.

Fair or not, agriculture – farm animals in particular – has become a large part of the conversation about climate change. The UK government estimates that agriculture constitutes 10 percent of UK greenhouse gas emissions. Of agricultural emissions, however, only 10 percent is carbon dioxide, with methane accounting for just under 60 percent and nitrous oxide around 30 percent.[1] Nitrous oxide emissions are a result of the use of nitrogen-based fertilisers.

Agricultural emissions have fallen sharply over the past three decades: 15 percent in the case of nitrous oxide and also methane; 26 percent in the case of CO_2 emissions. This is in part down to less fertiliser being used, especially on grassland, but also down to Britain producing less food. UK self-sufficiency in food (the amount of food produced in the country as a proportion of the food consumed) has declined sharply from 78 percent in 1984 to 60 percent in 2021.[2] This in turn has much to do with land being 'set aside' under the EU's Common Agricultural Policy (CAP) from the early 1990s onwards as well as a reform of CAP in the early 2000s which delinked agricultural subsidies from food production and simply rewarded ownership of farmland instead – a form of welfare for landowners.

If the decline in Britain's food self-sufficiency seems alarming, the net zero target threatens to push it down further still. Now that Britain is out of the EU, it no longer falls under the CAP. Instead, in early 2022 environment secretary George Eustice announced that the government would keep paying in the region of £3 billion a year to farmers but would henceforth do so in order to reward 'sustainable farming'. Some of the pay-outs would go to landowners who wish to 'rewild' land – i.e. take it out of agricultural production and return it to what our ancestors would have called waste.

A large part of the reasoning behind this is that it could allow large quantities of carbon to be sequestrated in the soil and foliage. To that end, the government has proposed to restore 280,000 hectares of the English countryside to peat bog by 2050 and, as already discussed, to plant trees at an annual rate of 7,500 hectares across England (and 30,000 hectares' worth across the UK) by 2025. It hasn't quite said how long it plans to maintain this rate of tree-planting, but if it carries on until 2050 it would mean 188,000 hectares of woodland created in England by 2050.[3] To put this into context, the surface area of England is 13.3 million hectares and the area utilised for agriculture – out of which total the area to be turned into bog and forest will have to come – is 9 million hectares. In our bid to store carbon in the soil, in other words, we will lose around one thirtieth of existing farmland. In a country which only produces around 60 percent of the food it consumes, this matters.

Yet it is less than many environmentalists would like – and a lot less than we would need to plant in order to cancel out Britain's lingering carbon emissions (as we saw in the last chapter we would need to cover over half of Britain's land surface in order to claim carbon neutrality over the next century). A campaign group, Rewilding Britain, has demanded that 30 percent of the land area of England be returned to nature by 2030 – a target which appears to have been plucked from the sky. There is, it has to be said, something rather appealing about turning intensively farmed land back to nature. Rewilding appears to be popular with the general public. But it does, needless to say, raise the issue of where our food is going to come from. If we are going to lose a thirtieth of farmland there would appear to be essentially three choices: either we maintain food production by farming even more intensively on the remaining land, we don't worry about producing our own food and accept that we will have to import more, or we try to manipulate the nation's diet by persuading – even forcing – people to consume food which is less land-hungry.

There seems to be little in the government's strategy to suggest that it is even looking for ways of achieving the first. There are ways that food production could be intensified, for example by taking inspiration from the vast glasshouses of the Netherlands, which succeed in producing fresh fruit and vegetables for much of the year – an idea which the government appeared to take up in its Food Strategy in June 2022. We could bring more livestock production into high-density, indoor environments, where the animals could be fed more controlled diets. As well as freeing up pasture for rewilding, this could have advantages in cutting methane emissions. If cattle were kept in large sheds, it would surely be possible to collect methane produced through their belching, and from decay of their manure, and to use it as a fuel.

Yet government policy does not seem to favour intensification of agriculture; indeed, it tends to steer in the other direction. Former environment secretary Michael Gove, for example, when challenged on reports that US 'industrial' farming would come to Britain as a result of Brexit, told the House of Commons 'One thing is clear: I do not want to see, and we will not have, US-style farming in this country'.[4] As so often on anything to do with net zero, the government seems to be nodding in multiple directions at once: embracing the idea of vast greenhouses on the one hand but rejecting the case for industrialised farming on the other.

But if we are going to import more food, any carbon emissions saved by taking agricultural land in Britain out of production and rewilding are likely to be cancelled out by emissions created elsewhere in the world in the name of producing food for UK consumers – as well as in transporting food to Britain.

As for the third possibility – that UK consumers be persuaded or cajoled into changing their diets to favour food which is less land-hungry – that is very much part of the Climate Change Committee's (CCC) plan for net zero. Among the scenarios it has presented is that by 2035 'diets change, reducing our consumption of high-carbon meat and dairy products by 20 percent by 2030 with further reductions in later years'. This, it claims, will allow Britain to produce as much food per head as it does now, in spite of 460,000 hectares of farmland being turned to woodland and a further 260,000 acres being switched from food to energy crops.[5]

The chairman of the committee, Lord Deben, has since denied that he is trying to turn Britain vegan or even vegetarian. On the contrary, in December 2021 he accused animal rights campaigners of 'muddying' the climate change issue by using it as an argument to give up meat altogether. Livestock farming, Deben went on, is essential for reducing emissions because grazing increases the ability of the soil to absorb carbon.[6] In other words, the CCC already appears to be rowing back a bit on its plans to drastically cut meat production.

Just how would government persuade people to change their diets if they did not really want to? A meat tax? The idea has proven extremely unpopular, not least because it would be highly regressive – the wealthy could carry on eating as before, while the poor were forced to cut back. Good luck to any government trying an alternative: to ration meat. The public, I suspect, would take a dim view of being taken back to the 1940s. In its own Net Zero Strategy, published in October 2021, the government doesn't even mention cutting back on meat.

What, in any case, would we really be trying to achieve by shrinking the beef industry? In Britain beef production is predominantly pasture-based, with 87 percent of beef cattle following forage-based diets, as opposed to eating prepared feed. Even when you take into account winter feed, grass forms 70 percent of their diets. Yet much of the land which they forage could not easily be turned over to producing crops for human consumption because it is too damp, too steep or the soil is too poor. According to the National Farmers' Union, 65 percent of farmland in Britain is best suited to pasture.[7] Some advocates of veganism like to claim that meat is a very inefficient way of feeding humans because we first have to feed the animals, using resources which we could have used to feed ourselves directly. That might be true when we feed cattle on soya, but it isn't true when we feed them on grass; cattle are fairly efficient machines for producing human food from land which could not otherwise be used to produce it, for turning a form of vegetation which is indigestible for humans into a foodstuff which can sustain us.

Conversely, many of the high-protein plant foods which form the basis of some vegan diets cannot easily be grown in Britain. Two thirds of the world's soya, for example, is currently grown in either the United States or Brazil, where it is widely blamed for deforestation. California is the dominant producer of the world's almonds, much of them in irrigated, water-stressed areas. We are forever being told how much water it takes to produce a pint of cow's milk (the vast majority of it 'green' water direct from rainfall), but rather less that it takes 158 litres of water to produce a litre of almond milk, most of it 'blue' water extracted from watercourses. The Canadian prairies are the largest producer of lentils, India the biggest supplier of chickpeas. These are not crops which are going to take well to misty, upland regions of Wales and the West Country. If you want to switch Britons from omnivorous diets to vegan ones you are going to end up with an awful lot of abandoned pasture land and a sharp increase in food imports. The irony is that many of the people who call for a switch to vegan diets to help the climate will, on another day, be demanding that we consume more locally grown food. Yet what they advocate would result in the opposite. This is before we even come to considering the nutritional issues of vegan diets, which can only be mitigated through food supplements. That, too, is an industry with a carbon footprint.

The vegan issue exposes a very common phenomenon in the climate change debate: that there are a large number of activists who will always jump to the hairshirt solutions – the ones that involve people stopping doing things, curtailing their lifestyles, impoverishing themselves (although the activists might claim that a simpler life is a richer one). Such people play to a gallery of the relatively well-off – who don't have to worry where their next meal is coming from, who don't have to struggle to keep their homes warm and for whom the idea of getting back to nature is an aesthetic diversion (although perhaps in practice limited to a few days' glamping at the Glastonbury Festival every year). Contained within this philosophy is a messianic drive – pleasure, even – in trying to tell other people how to live their lives. Climate change has rekindled a kind of primitive socialism – it is William Morris's arts and crafts movement repackaged for the 21st century, claiming science as its basis. Yet those who follow this philosophy tend to react very strongly when they are confronted with any scientific or technological solution to cutting greenhouse gases without making people poorer. It spoils their narrative: that humans must be punished for their excesses and that we can only save ourselves via a return to a simpler existence.

Agriculture presents a big challenge to this philosophy because there are potentially many solutions to cutting greenhouse gas emissions which do not involve us having to restrict our diet or compromise our lifestyles in any way. Take methane production from cattle, for example. Dutch company DSM is developing a cattle feed additive called Bovaer which suppresses the production of enzymes which cause methane emission in cattle – a quarter of a teaspoon per animal per day, it claims, can reduce methane emissions for dairy cattle by 30 percent and from beef cattle by up to 90 percent.[8] A University of California study found that feeding cattle 80 grammes of seaweed per day in addition to their normal diet reduced methane emissions by 82 percent.[9] As for cattle manure, a New Zealand company, Ravensdown, has developed a system for treating effluent ponds with iron sulphate to cut methane production by 99 percent.[10]

Or why not collect the methane produced on farms and use it as a fuel? Methane is, after all, the main component of natural gas. Farm machinery manufacturer New Holland has marketed a methane-powered tractor, designed to run on fuel produced on the farm from manure and other farm waste. This can be produced in an anaerobic digester. Where cattle and other animals are kept in controlled indoor environments it must also be possible to collect methane produced by the animals' flatulence.

All these technologies have costs, of course, and as they are at an early stage of development we don't know whether they will really turn out to be economical. Yet there is a sizeable element of the environmental movement which doesn't really want to know about them – it simply wants us to adopt 'plant-based diets'. This is ideology; it is not a contribution to the debate on net zero.

What about the nitrous oxides produced by nitrogen-based fertilisers used in arable farming? Fine, some will say, let's go organic. Except, that is, that organic farming has historically relied upon manure from farm animals. And if we reduce the numbers of farm animals? We would be facing serious diminution of yields – with the result that we would have to import foods, such as wheat and potatoes, in which we currently have reasonably good self-sufficiency.

Rewilding is not the only pressure being put on farmland. We are also losing land to solar farms – and very good-quality farmland at that. According to the campaign group Net Zero Watch, there were, in early 2022, 37 GW worth of solar farms either under construction or in the planning stage. Together, they proposed to cover 150,000 acres, or 234 square miles.[11] Much of this land, such as on the Cambridgeshire/Suffolk border, is quality farmland used at present for horticulture – land which you might think was rather important if we were going to turn to more plant-based diets.

There is a far faster and easier way that Britain could get close to zero emissions from agriculture, but it isn't one which would benefit the planet, still less help employment, the balance of payments or national food security. It is to offshore the entire agricultural industry and its emissions with it – and rewild Britain's former farmland. Thanks to the government's accounting trick – which as we have discussed includes only territorial emissions for the purpose of its net zero target – this is all too likely to form a large part of the government's solution to reach net zero as it is forced into desperate measures to fulfil its legal obligation.

A rational food policy for Britain would look at all threats to national well-being – not just climate change – and come to the conclusion that national food security ought to be given a far higher priority than it has been given in recent decades. Between 1945 and the mid-1980s it was indeed granted huge importance – thanks not least because the experience of the Second World War, when German U-boats targeted transatlantic food convoys in an attempt to starve Britain into submission, was still fairly fresh in the memory. Since the 1980s, on the other hand, agricultural policy has worked on the assumption that in a world that is open to trade it no longer makes sense to target national food security: we will always be able to buy what we need on global markets, and therefore resources in Britain would be better put to more profitable ventures – a classic case of comparative advantage.

Maybe, but the double crises of Covid-19 and the Russian invasion of Ukraine in 2022 – a country long known as Europe's bread basket for its cereal production – have reminded us that we cannot always take uninterrupted global trade for granted, and that we need some kind of plan for how we cope in a situation where parts of the world suddenly close down.

Moreover, failing to draw up a proper policy for national food security is somewhat at odds with many of the statements that government ministers and government agencies have been making about climate change and its impact on food production in many parts of the world. 'Crop yields are expected to decline with climate change,' states the Meteorological Office on its website. 'Some parts of the world where crops can be grown today may find it harder to grow crops in future,' environment secretary George Eustice declared in December 2021.[12]

If that is what you really fear, surely you would want to ask yourself how Britain can maximise its agricultural production to protect against a decline in global food production – looking at what foods the British landscape is best at producing. That would inexorably lead you back to the conclusion that a country with a damp, maritime climate with many upland areas in its northern and western sides is well suited to mixed agriculture, with animals grazing lands which would be very difficult to convert to arable production.

It is often asserted that climate change will itself harm our ability to feed ourselves – this being used as further justification for eradicating all emissions by 2050. Higher temperatures, more droughts, more floods; all, it is claimed, will hinder crop yields and reduce agricultural production.

The idea that crop yields are going to crash in a warmer world has been widely promoted, not least thanks to modelling published by the US government. A Stanford University study in 2021 claimed that average crop yields (per hectare) could plunge by between 3 and 12 percent by 2050 and by between 11 and 25 percent by 2090.[13] A NASA study, too, claims that climate change will begin to impact on crop yields 'within 10 years', with maize yields falling by 24 percent – although wheat yields could rise by 17 percent.[14] Models reach this conclusion, it says, thanks to higher temperatures and greater tendency towards drought.

Are these claims realistic? These two studies claim to look into the future, yet back in the real world, yields are still increasing sharply. The UN Food and Agriculture Organization has compiled statistics of average global crop yields since 1961 – a period over which the world has seen rising temperatures. If they have affected our ability to grow food it doesn't quite show up in the figures:[15]

Crop	Yield increase (%), 2011–2020	Yield increase (%), 1961–2020
Potatoes	10.3	78
Bananas	15.2	116
Maize	11.9	196
Rice	3.5	145
Wheat	9.8	219
Soybeans	10.3	147

The only crop which it found had suffered over the past decade was cassava, yields of which fell by 8.5 percent between 2011 and 2020. But even in this case they were up 47 percent since 1961. Why the increase in yields, when we are supposedly already suffering from climate change-induced droughts and floods? Obviously, the climate isn't the only variable in how much food we produce. Improved methods, machinery, selective breeding of plants, better irrigation, fertilisers, pesticides and genetic modification (GM) of crops have all contributed to increased yields. Won't we continue to get better at growing crops, so as to negate any negative effects of climate change? The NASA study doesn't even try to take this into account, stating 'These models do not address economic incentives, changing farming practices, and adaptations such as breeding hardier crop varieties'. As we have seen, the quest for net zero depends on all kinds of new technologies being invented or scaled up over the next 27 years. Yet a study supposed to inform the world on the effects of climate change on agriculture works on the assumption that technology is frozen in time. In reality, not only will we get better at producing food – or at least we will if we allow ourselves to explore new methods, which in the case of GM crops most of Europe has prevented itself from doing – but there will inevitably be some benefits from warmer temperatures, too, to offset some of the downsides. Some parts of the world which cannot be cultivated now, either because they are too dry or too cold, will become able to be farmed – offsetting parts of the world where agriculture might become more difficult. Moreover, plants are rather fond of carbon dioxide – it is, after all, their food. Air which is richer in CO_2 promotes the growth of plants. 'Vertical farms', which grow vegetables in controlled indoor conditions, tend to pump in extra CO_2 to a concentration of around 1,000 parts per million (ppm) compared with just over 400 ppm in normal air.[16]

As so often with climate change, the modelling seems to have acquired a life of its own, and is quite at odds with real-world observation. Yet it is the modelling – the product of questionable assumptions and crude attempts to simulate a complex real world – which invariably seems to win the battle for public attention. It becomes treated as a fact that climate change is causing agricultural yields to collapse – when the data tells us that so far, at least, the opposite is true: yields are rapidly increasing. Learned figures have been predicting mass starvation ever since Thomas Malthus in the 18th century; climate change is just the latest manifestation of this philosophy of doom. The tendency for debate on climate change to be driven by exaggeration, worst-case scenarios and faulty modelling is something we will examine next.

15.

Listen to the scientists

WE HAVE NEVER HAD A proper national debate on whether or not to impose a legally binding requirement to reach net zero greenhouse gas emissions by 2050 because every time the subject is raised it gets closed down. The line advanced by the government, as well as by many MPs, outside bodies and some newspapers and broadcasters is that we are facing such a climatic cataclysm that we simply cannot afford not to achieve the 2050 target. Never mind that there is no point in Britain and a few other countries pursuing the target on their own. Never mind the issue of costs and practicalities. We have to do this. Argument over.

And if we weren't quite able to eliminate net greenhouse gas emissions by 2050? The walls of civilisation would fall in – quite literally according to English Heritage, whose senior estate manager, launching a £1 million funding campaign in September 2021, claimed that historic buildings were at risk from 'higher temperatures throughout the year, longer periods of extreme heat, combined with more rainfall in winter, heavier rain in winter and summer . . .'[1] Never mind that buildings in warmer climates seem to avoid the wet rot which attacks those in Britain . . .

That is just one fairly random example of the endless stories of doom. There is virtually no ill in the world which has not been blamed on climate change; from ending white Christmases (according to a BBC report, citing the Met Office),[2] to shrinking the human frame (University of Cambridge),[3] to wiping out six billion people (Emeritus professor in human ecology at the University of British Columbia).[4] Even worse, it could mean the end of tomato ketchup, as the yields of processing tomatoes grown in the United States, China and Italy decline (Aarhus University).[5] Climate change will in future cause kidney stones (according to the Children's Hospital of Philadelphia)[6] and increase obesity in children (according to a *Guardian* article citing Israeli research).[7]

A coalition of councils in Glasgow claims that it will need £184 million to cope with climate change.[8] The average daily maximum temperature in the Scottish city in July is 19.8 degrees Celsius. Even if the world warmed by 4 degrees Celsius – which would be four times the measured increase over the past century and a half – Glasgow would still only reach the typical summer temperatures currently experienced in London.

There is ample evidence that the Earth is warming, and there are potentially many negative consequences from that. Yet hyperbole now rules so much coverage of climate change. Changes which are benign are regularly hyped-up into something ominous, and rarely is it admitted that there might even be some benefits from a warming climate. On 19 July 2022 Britain experienced its highest-ever recorded temperature: 40.3 degrees Celsius recorded at Coningsby, Lincolnshire, with similar temperatures recorded across eastern and south-eastern England. The event – which was successfully forecast a week in advance – marked the fourth time that Britain's maximum temperature record had been broken since 1990 and is consistent with a warming climate. Heatwaves are one of the forms of adverse weather for which there is evidence of an increasing trend. Yet did that justify the reporting which framed it as an 'apocalypse'? Did it justify the predictions by the government's former Chief Scientific Advisor, Sir David King, that the heatwave could cause 10,000 excess deaths?[9]

It is true that hot weather often leads to excess deaths; a study of the less intense but much more prolonged 1976 heatwave in Britain found that deaths registered in Birmingham swelled by nearly 20 percent during the period 24 June to 8 July. When the Office for National Statistics (ONS) published an analysis of excess deaths in the hot periods of the summer of 2022, it recorded 2,227 excess deaths during the main period of heatwave between the 10th and 25th of July, and a total of 3,271 excess deaths over the five periods of hot weather that summer – representing a 6.2 percent rise on what might be called normal levels of deaths for those periods.[10] It was a lot lower than King had predicted, but even then there are caveats to consider. The ONS figures for excess deaths are a crude comparison with the average deaths of the past five years (although the ONS excludes the pandemic year of 2020). Given that the population is growing to the tune of 0.5 percent, and is ageing so that the population of over-70s is growing by around two percent a year, you would expect the number of deaths to grow year on year. Moreover, the middle of 2022 witnessed a large, unexplained number of excess deaths, during cool periods as well as hot periods, beginning in March, long before any heatwave.[11] Pressure on NHS A&E departments as hospitals attempt to catch up with a backlog of treatments hanging over from the Covid-19 pandemic has been suggested as a factor. It is also worth noting that the excess deaths among the under-70s actually turned negative during the hot periods, and that excess deaths fell sharply in the days after each heatwave ended – suggesting that the hot weather brought forward deaths which were imminent anyway.

But let us accept that heatwaves are a danger to health and that climate change is making heatwaves more common and more intense. The increased risk must be balanced against a fall in deaths from the cold – which is a much bigger killer in Britain's climate. When the ONS studied real data for the first 20 years of the 21st century, it failed to detect any increase in deaths from heatwaves – in spite of new high-temperature records for Britain being set in 2003 and 2019. What it did find, on the other hand, was that deaths from the cold had fallen. In fact, over the course of 20 years the upward trend in temperatures in England and Wales appeared to have resulted in 555,103 fewer temperature-related deaths.[12] The headlines ought to have read: 'Climate Change Saves Half a Million Lives', yet this real-word data seemed to tease out some rare scepticism from news outlets more used to presenting doom-laden forecasts and scenarios as established fact. BBC Climate Editor Justin Rowlatt began his analysis of the study with the words 'statistics can be slippery'. In other words, he was saying, I'm choosing not to believe this particular set of data.

What subsequently happened to this study is rather fasci-nating, because it follows what happens so often with data which is inconvenient to the narrative of cataclysmic climate change. In May 2022 the ONS issued a statement with the words: 'Please note an error has been identified in calculating the number of "fewer cold days" in the period 2001 to 2020. This has resulted in a significant overestimate in the number of fewer cold day deaths. This happened because of human error.' When I asked the ONS for an explanation, it said that 'external reviewers' had spotted the error and stated that 'in further developing our methodology we continue to work with subject experts in the climate change field' – which was rather odd because surely if you are trying to measure deaths from the heat and the cold it is medical experts that you need, not climate ones. Whether you want to believe the ONS's climate mortality statistics or not, they echo the ONS's sepa-rately published figures on excess winter deaths which also show a long downward trajectory in the extra number of deaths witnessed in the colder months of the year (reversed in the Covid winter of 2020/21) – although they continue to outnumber the deaths in the summer months.[13] So, no, mortality data does not support the case that the British climate is becoming more lethal. Quite the opposite – a milder climate appears to be accompanied by (I won't say the cause of, because there are other factors at play) a fall in temperature-related deaths.

There were no such doubts in evidence, no such challenge to the methodology, when news sources reported, on the same day as the ONS temperature-related mortality data was published, the government's efforts to quantify the effect of climate change on the economy. 'Climate change to cost UK economy up to £20bn a year by 2050,'[14] claimed a headline in *The Times*. The study had attempted to estimate changes in weather from models and somehow tried to imagine how these might affect the climate – without really knowing what kind of weather or economy we will have in 2050.

Actually, the government's climate change risk assessment did identify some benefits from climate change, such as the ability to grow a richer variety of crops in Britain, but this tended to go missing from the reporting. Moreover, some of the disbenefits identified made you wonder: are we really so helpless as to be unable to cope? It cited as 'high risk', for example, 'risks to people and the economy from climate-related failure of the power system'.[15] But why should the power system in Britain become more vulnerable as a result of higher temperatures? Much hotter countries than Britain manage to maintain power grids. A bigger and more immediate threat to power supplies is that posed by a poorly configured electricity generation system as the country rushes towards renewables without properly addressing the problem of intermittency.

The government's climate assessment goes on to cite 'risks to human health, wellbeing and productivity from increased exposure to heat in homes and other buildings'. Yet people already live and work quite happily in buildings in climates far hotter than Britain will experience even in the most dramatic scenarios of climate change. They manage to do this thanks in part to properly designed buildings, insulated from heat as well as cold, aided by proper ventilation and air conditioning. The trouble is that in Britain we have been putting up some very poorly engineered new buildings which are designed to cut carbon emissions to the exclusion of all other considerations, such as the comfort of their occupants. They are stuffed with insulation and sealed against drafts – yet have inadequate ventilation and insufficient means to disperse solar gain and heat emanating from appliances and human occupants. As put by the Zero Carbon Hub – a now-defunct government initiative set up to promote buildings with net zero emissions – 'There appears to be growing evidence of overheating in homes, particularly for newer homes built to satisfy more demanding standards of energy efficiency'.[16] In other words, occupants of new homes are wilting not because of climate change but, perversely, because of building standards designed to avert climate change. It might not affect the whole housing stock, but it is a poor reflection on our ability to adapt to climate change.

Nuances such as this are increasingly being lost as we are fed a diet of ever-greater climatic doom. There seem to be some very simple rules behind the climate change narrative being spun to the public. Firstly, that climate change offers nothing positive, only harm. Secondly, that the only way to tackle that harm is to end climate change; the concept of adaptation is sacrilege. We end up not with changes to the climate which might be managed – but cataclysms which will be beyond human ingenuity, and beyond the ability of the natural world, to cope with. Climate change is apparently going to kill off plants which rely on birds to spread their seeds.[17] It is going to kill off insects, half of which are in danger of losing half their current habitable range – except for mosquitos and locusts, whose numbers are going to explode.[18]

There is no extreme weather event now which does not get blamed on climate change. Take, for example, the exchange in the House of Commons following Storm Arwen in November 2021, which caused long power outages in Scotland and the North of England. Labour's shadow climate change secretary Ed Miliband declared that 'faced with the climate crisis, extreme weather events will sadly become all the more common in the future', to which the government's business secretary Kwasi Kwarteng replied: 'Clearly Storm Arwen was an event the likes of which we haven't seen for certainly 60 years since the record starts. We have to be prepared for similarly extreme, difficult weather conditions in the future.'[19]

Were they fair things to say? While Arwen was a strong storm and brought gales from the north, rather than, as is more common, from the west and southwest, there was nothing unprecedented about Arwen, and neither was it, as we shall see, part of a trend towards a stormier Britain. One way to judge a storm is to look at the maximum gust speed measured anywhere in its path. In the case of Storm Arwen the maximum gust speed (at low level) was 98 mph measured at Brizlee Wood in Northumberland, while a gust of 117 mph was measured on the Cairnwell, a mountain in the Cairngorms. How does that compare with the historical record? As for the Brizlee Wood reading, it did not even break the record for Northumberland: two more ferocious gusts were measured at Lynemouth of 102 mph on 16 January 1984 and 107 mph on 17 December 1979. As for the high-level reading, it didn't come even close to matching the 173 mph recorded on the summit of Cairngorm mountain itself on 20 March 1986. There have been many stronger winds measured in Scotland at lower levels in recent decades, with 142 mph recorded at Fraserburgh on 13 February 1989. To attribute Arwen to climate change was no more than lazy assertion, and one which went unchallenged, in spite of UK parliamentary democracy taking a dim view of ministers who mislead the House of Commons. It is easy, however, to see why it should have suited a government minister to claim the damage from Storm Arwen was a product of a crazed climate – rather than draw attention to an insufficiently robust electricity distribution network. What better way to fob off the occupants of the 31,000 homes who had just spent a fourth night without power?[20]

Some of what passes for warnings on climate is nothing more than flight of fancy. In January 2022 a study funded by the Met Office Climate Resilience Programme, and written by academics at the Universities of Exeter and Edinburgh, presented five scenarios as to what might happen by the year 2100, depending on what actions were taken now. One of them – in which the government carried on exploiting fossil fuels – bizarrely had Britain descending into hunter-gathering and feudal warfare. Another, where green policies were adopted, resulted in the eradication of poverty by the end of the century.[21] This is not climate science, nor science of any kind; it is plain fantasy fiction, dreamed up to serve a particular political outlook.

None of this is to say that climate change is not happening and is not a problem. The world is warming and there are many reasons why we should want to cut carbon emissions and adopt cleaner forms of energy. But we are not having a reasoned debate as to the choices and balances which that entails. Instead, we are presented with hysteria, with terms like 'heat apocalypse' being thrown about.[22] That belongs to the movies, not real life.

We are in this position partly because sceptical views have been all but banned from many newspapers and news channels. For example, in 2018 the BBC's head of news and current affairs, Fran Unsworth, sent a memo announcing a change as to how the broadcaster would in future report climate change – this following a ruling by the broadcast regulator Ofcom that the BBC's radio morning news programme *Today* had failed properly to challenge former Chancellor of the Exchequer Lord Lawson when he had appeared on the programme to provide a counter-view to a film made by Al Gore. BBC staff were now asked to complete a one-hour course on reporting climate change. The course made clear that interviewees who were sceptical about man-made climate change – which includes some notable climate scientists, even if the weight of opinion is on the other side – were no longer regularly to be invited onto BBC news programmes. It went further: sceptics were now being branded as 'deniers' – an emotive term coined by climate activists to try to compare their opponents to Holocaust deniers.[23]

'To achieve impartiality,' BBC news staff were told, 'you do not need to include outright deniers of climate change in BBC coverage, in the same way as you would not have someone denying that Manchester United won 2–0 last Saturday. The referee has spoken.'

In practice it isn't just 'outright deniers of climate change' who have disappeared from the BBC; I struggle to recall a single case where a dissenting opinion has been expressed on the subject on the *Today* programme, Radio 4's flagship morning news programme, over the past five years. Yet there appears to be no parallel ban on including the views of people who exaggerate the findings of the IPCC or other respectable scientific sources. On the contrary, such people have continued to appear on the BBC, their assertions left unchallenged. In September 2021, for example, Zoe Cohen, an activist with a group called Insulate Britain, which was then causing havoc by blocking motorways in and around London, was heard on the *Today* programme claiming that climate change would lead to 'the loss of all that we cherish, our society, our way of life and law and order', that the economy was 'in serious danger of collapse' and that climate change was 'endangering billions of people's lives'. On none of these claims was she challenged.[24]

In November 2021, to coincide with COP26, the BBC broadcast a *Panorama* programme called *Wild Weather: Our World Under Threat*, which claimed, among other things, that weather-related deaths around the world were increasing. Six months later the corporation's Executive Complaints Unit was driven to admit that this claim was false – the prevalence of weather-related deaths around the world has fallen as societies have become better at coping with extreme weather. It also found against another claim in the programme, that Madagascar was on the brink of suffering the first famine cause by climate change. The island, it ruled, had suffered from lower than average rainfall in recent years, but that there were other factors involved in food shortages.[25] Although the BBC didn't spell out what these other factors were, an earlier UN report had explained that, besides drought, the famine had been caused by Covid-19 restrictions which had prevented seasonal agricultural workers taking up jobs as they would usually do.[26]

There is a drive on the part of some environmental activists to go further than simply banish sceptical opinion from the airwaves of the BBC and the like. Trygve Lavik, a philosopher at the University of Bergen, has even suggested that what he calls climate change 'denialism' be made illegal on the grounds that it is a 'crime against present and future generations' – and that there are 'better reasons to outlaw climate denialism than Holocaust denialism'.[27] In doing so he manages to fuse two deplorable and growing traits in political activism: firstly, the tendency for all debate, on whatever subject, to gravitate towards Hitler and the Nazis, and secondly, a refusal to engage in argument with people with whom you disagree, rather to try to ban them from expressing their point of view. What does it say about your confidence in the merits of your own arguments that you feel the need to have them protected by law? Moreover, if you are concerned about falsehoods being disseminated on the internet, shouldn't that also include alarmist claims? But no, it was only 'denialism' which seemed to bother Lavik, as with so many others who claim to be standing up for truth.

Reporting on extreme weather in the press and broadcast media has undergone a notable change in mood in recent years. Reports rarely used to mention climate change, or when they did they would make the point – reinforced by many meteorologists themselves – that you cannot attribute any one weather event to climate change. In recent years, however, they have suddenly started blaming climate change at every opportunity. And, as with Kwasi Kwarteng's erroneous claim that Storm Arwen was unprecedented in the past 60 years, many of the claims made do not stand up to examination.

The change in tone is partly down to an organisation called Covering Climate Now, which started in 2019 as an initiative by the *Guardian* in association with the *Columbia Journalism Review*, the *Nation* and WNYC, and has been supercharged with donations from charitable trusts which have traditionally supported left-liberal causes.

The existence of Covering Climate Now wouldn't matter very much had it not persuaded some very high-profile news organisations to sign up for its campaign, including Bloomberg, Reuters, Al Jazeera, STV, *Channel 4 News*, *New Scientist*, the *Daily Mirror*, *Scientific American* and *Newsweek*. Journalists at all these organisations, according to Covering Climate Now, 'join a supportive community where they can expand their reporting opportunities, collaborate with fellow journalists, and forge a path towards an all newsroom approach to climate reporting'.

Covering Climate Now offers reporters what it calls 'resources'. You might think these might be links to important pieces of climate research. But one of the first things you get to on its website is a style guide. 'Remember, an extreme weather story that doesn't mention climate change is *incomplete* and potentially even *inaccurate*,' it asserts. 'Here's some simple language to help,' it goes on to proffer, suggesting that reporters append their stories with the words: 'This [hurricane] comes at a time when human-caused climate change is consistently making storms like it more intense.'[28]

This is not the conclusion that would be reached by a reporter who bothers to do their own research. The National Oceanic and Atmospheric Administration (NOAA), which has done more research into this than anyone, affirms that 'it is premature to conclude with high confidence that human-caused increases in greenhouse gases have had a detectable impact on past Atlantic basin hurricane activity that is outside the range of natural variability'. Further, it states 'there is no strong evidence of century-scale increasing trends in U.S. landfalling hurricanes or major hurricanes'. The same is true, it says, of Atlantic 'basin-wide' hurricanes – i.e. Atlantic hurricanes which do not make landfall in the United States. It goes on to state that climate models do predict future changes in hurricane activity. If temperatures reach 2 degrees Celsius above late 19th-century levels, it says, we might expect maximum wind speed in a hurricane to increase by between 1 and 10 percent, and rainfall to increase by between 10 and 15 percent. The proportion of tropical storms reaching grades 4 and 5, it says, is expected to increase, although this does not necessarily mean that we will have more grade 4 and 5 hurricanes in total, because the overall number of tropical storms is expected either to stay the same or to fall.[29]

The IPCC Sixth Assessment Report presents a similarly mixed picture of trends. Australia, it found, is currently experiencing the lowest frequency of tropical cyclones in the past 550 to 1,500 years. The northern Indian Ocean is seeing an increased intensity of the most severe storms but a decrease in frequency of storms overall. In the United States there has been an observed fall in the 'translation speed' of hurricanes – i.e. the speed at which the storm moves when it hits land – resulting in heavier rainfall in some coastal areas. It is a similar picture for the storms in extra-tropical latitudes which affect Britain. As for the North Atlantic the IPCC concludes 'the number of cyclones with very low central pressure increased from 1979 to 1990 and then declined until 2010'. Moreover, 'the observed intensity of extreme winds is becoming less severe in the low to mid-latitudes, while becoming more severe in high latitudes poleward of 60 degrees'.[30]

So that is what the data tells us: that no, rising global temperatures have not unleashed lethal hurricanes and other storms which otherwise wouldn't have occurred – although the models claim we might expect some change in hurricane intensity in future. In some parts of the world there is a downward trend in storm activity. Yet that is not the picture that many casual viewers, listeners and readers will have picked up from reports of extreme weather events. Rather they may have taken it as indisputable fact that the world is already in the grip of mad winds whipped up as a result of human influence on the climate, that when anyone dies or is made homeless in a hurricane they are victims of man-made climate change and that things are only going to get worse unless we take drastic action now. Were the public to be fed a calmer, more even-handed reporting of the data we might have a more rational debate over net zero.

So what is really going on with the climate? What, exactly, is at stake when people assert that climate change is so dire a threat that we have no option other than to eliminate all net greenhouse emissions by 2050? We will look at two sources – sources, presumably, which inform the UK government's policy on climate change: the Sixth Assessment Report of the Intergovernmental Panel on Climate Change (IPCC) and the

Royal Meteorological Society's State of the Climate Report, the latter of which is particular to Britain.[31]

In common with global data from multiple sources, the Royal Meteorological Society records an upward trend in UK temperatures over the past 60 years. The average for the decade 2012–21 was 1.0 degree Celsius higher than for the period 1961–90. An accompanying graph shows that much of the rise in temperatures in Britain occurred in the 1980s and 1990s, with a much shallower trend since the turn of the century. As for heatwaves, the record for the highest-recorded temperature has been broken several times in recent decades, and all but one of the hottest ten days recorded in Britain have occurred since 1990. Until 1990, the highest-recorded temperature in Britain was 36.7 degrees Celsius in Northamptonshire on 9 August 1911; it now stands at 40.3 degrees Celsius recorded in Coningsby, Lincolnshire, on 19 July 2022. That is one measure of a heatwave; another is its duration – and heatwaves of recent years have tended to be intense but short. The fabled heatwave of June/July 1976 included 15 consecutive days where the temperature somewhere in England exceeded 90 degrees Fahrenheit (32.2 degrees Celsius). In July 2022 this threshold was passed on only three days. The State of the Climate Report includes the concept of 'cooling degree days' to measure heatwaves: an integration of temperature over time defined as the sum of degrees above 22 degrees Celsius over a period of time (they are called 'cooling degree days' because they are trying to measure the need for cooling in the form of air conditioning). This metric shows a steady upward trend since 1960 – i.e. we are seeing more heatwaves – yet it also shows the 1976 heatwave as recording more cooling degree days than for any year in the past 60 years. Second is 1995, with recent heatwaves showing lower spikes.

As for extreme low temperatures, the State of the Climate Report uses a mirror concept in the form of 'heating degree days' which combine the intensity and duration of low temperatures. These show a pronounced fall over the past 60 years, with a very sharp fall between 1980 and 2000 followed by a flatter downward trend in the years since.

Average rainfall was 10 percent higher for the decade 2012–21 than during the period 1961–90 – an expected consequence of rising temperatures given that warmer air can hold more moisture. Temperatures have risen across the year. The increase in rainfall, by contrast, has been concentrated in winter and summer, with no obvious trend in spring or autumn. In the decade 2012–21, it states, winter rainfall was on average 26 percent higher than in the reference period 1961–90 and summer rainfall an average of 15 percent higher.

The latter figure stands out because it is contrary to the climate models which have consistently suggested that Britain will see drier summers as global temperatures increase. For example, in 2009 the UK government issued a document predicting that summer precipitation across the UK would fall by between 17 percent and 23 percent by the 2080s, with falls of up to 40 percent in parts of southern England.[32] We are not in the 2080s yet, but, while we have had some dry summers, the current trend is firmly in the opposite direction, which ought to raise questions about the usefulness of climate models – but the discrepancy seems to have gone largely unnoticed.

Similarly, contrary to the claims made every time Britain experiences windy weather, the incidence of damaging winds in Britain is on a downward trend. The State of the Climate Report notes: 'There have been fewer occurrences of maximum gust speeds exceeding 40/50/60 Kt [46/58/69 mph] for the last two decades compared to the 1980s and 1990s.' It goes on to observe that wind speeds generally have been falling in Britain, as they have been across the world, with a downward trend in annual mean speeds since 1969. As for extreme rainfall, there are several ways to measure it. One metric is the number of days per year when rainfall averaged across Britain exceeds the 95th or 99th percentile of wet days. On this measure, Britain experienced an increase in extreme rainfall between 1960 and the end of the century, but with a flat trend since. The State of the Climate Report also measures the number of occasions when any weather station in Britain measures a total of 50 mm or more of rain. On this measure, the trend has continued to increase since 2000. However, there is a problem with the data, as the study admits. The number of rain gauges across Britain has fallen over recent decades (remarkably, given the importance in recording climatic trends) and, while the study has tried to correct for this, the authors note 'we cannot rule out the possibility that the present day network while having fewer stations overall may provide better sampling of regions that experience higher frequency of heavy rain days such as western Scotland'.

Unsurprisingly, given the general rise in temperatures, Britain has seen a decreasing trend in the number of days of air frost and snow lying at low altitudes. Year to year variability, however, is very high – the year with the highest number of frosts across the UK was 2010, with more even than during the famously harsh winter of 1963. Britain has also become sunnier, especially in winter and spring. This may be a reflection of lower air pollution.

There is one very firm trend: rising sea levels. Since the start of the 20th century mean sea levels around Britain have risen by 165 mm – just over 1.5 mm per year. A faster trend of 3.6 mm per year is quoted for between 1993 and 2019. The trend, though, is far from smooth, and the early 1990s just happen to have seen a temporary but pronounced dip in mean sea levels.

Those, then, are the observed changes in the UK climate over recent decades – not the results of predictive modelling but real data. They confirm an upward trend in temperature and rainfall – and we can reasonably suppose that these trends are connected with higher levels of greenhouse gases in the atmosphere, even if we can't prove it. As for 'extreme' weather, they bear out that Britain is experiencing more heatwaves but also fewer cold spells. There is some evidence of more intense rainfall. Other than that, they cannot be said to support the idea that Britain is suffering extreme or 'violent' weather, 'climate breakdown' or any other of the hysterical claims which are being made every time Britain suffers weather-related damage. Indeed, the prevalence of damaging winds is on a downward trend.

How much do we need to worry about any of this? Trends in temperature and rainfall will, if maintained throughout this century, give Britain the kind of climate which is already experienced in slightly more southerly latitudes. A further rise of 1.5 degrees Celsius in average July temperatures in London, for example, would take us to the current levels experienced in Paris. If peak rainfall were to rise, too, it would hardly be impossible to cope with this through better drains and watercourses. But of all challenges presented by climate change, sea level rise is the most serious – at least in Britain's case. Many of the country's most populated areas are in low-lying coastal locations, not least London, which sits at the end of a funnelling estuary vulnerable to tidal surges. Even now, parts of East London, South Essex and North Kent lie below sea level, with some marsh areas only kept dry thanks to sea walls and pumped drainage systems. In an unlikely worst-case scenario – a tidal surge of 2.7 metres, combined with failure of flood defences – the Environment Agency calculates that parts of Central London, south of the Thames, could flood to a depth of 4 metres.[33] Clearly, the sea already is, and always has been, a risk to London – and rising sea levels add to the challenge of flood defence. According to tidal studies by the University of Southampton, mean sea levels rose in the Thames by an average of 3.6 mm a year between 1990 and 2018. Its modelling indicates that a total rise of 1.15 metres between 1990 and 2100 is 'within the range of possible outcomes'.[34]

Yet climate change is not the whole story here. Britain sits on a tectonic plate. The southeast of England is sinking – and has been sinking since the end of the last ice age – while the northwest of Scotland is rising. In recent years satellite measurements have made it possible to quantify this with some accuracy. According to the British Geological Survey, between 1997 and 2005 the land around the Thames Estuary sank by between 0.9 mm and 1.5 mm per year – and up to 2.1 mm in the case of land formed of one particular type of deposit.[35] In other words, up to half the change in apparent sea level in the Thames Estuary is down to the land sinking rather than the sea rising. While London is at an increasing risk of flooding, it is not a case of a city which has suddenly been put at risk by man-made climate change. Even if we could stop sea levels from rising by halting carbon emissions tomorrow (and we couldn't), we would still have to cope with an existing and increasing risk of flooding in London, due to the sinking land. As we shall see later, we are putting rather less effort into this problem than we might be – and certainly a whole lot less money and effort than we are putting into reaching our arbitrary deadline of net zero by 2050.

But of course Britain is only one small part of the world. What about the global perspective? Is there anything in climate science to suggest that the Hollywood scenario – in which coastal cities are swamped with tidal waves, the world burns (except for the bits which freeze) and we are all swept away by mad hurricanes – is remotely likely? Let's have a look at the IPCC Sixth Assessment Report (AR6).

'Code red for humanity' were the words which accompanied

much coverage of the report when it was published in August 2021. They were not words from the report itself but from a press conference given by the UN Secretary-General, António Guterres. The report asserted that the IPCC is surer than it had ever been that human activities are warming the planet; but no, the world hasn't turned red hot. The mean global surface temperature of the Earth, concludes AR6, has risen by 0.99 degrees Celsius since 1850–1900 – 1.59 degrees Celsius over land and 0.88 degrees Celsius over ocean. It is 'likely', it goes on to say, that emissions of greenhouse gases have had a warming effect somewhere between 1 and 2 degrees Celsius, but that this has been countered by emissions of aerosols, which have had a cooling effect of 0.8 degrees Celsius. Global temperatures, it goes on to say, have risen faster in the past 50 years than in any comparable period during the past 2,000 years. Temperatures are now higher than they were during the last multi-century warm period, when they were between 0.2 and 1.0 degrees Celsius warmer than 1850–1900, and are higher than at any point since 125,000 years ago.

AR6 reveals that the atmospheric concentration of CO_2 has risen from 315 parts per million (ppm) in 1959 to 414 ppm in 2020. It asserts that this can be directly linked to the burning of fossil fuels because of the changing balance of carbon isotopes present in the air. As for melting ice – one of the central themes of so much climate coverage – the IPCC notes that the extent of Arctic sea ice has decreased since the 1970s by 40 percent in September (the month when it usually reaches its minimum) and 10 percent in March (the month it usually reaches its maximum), that it is 'very likely' that a loss of ice cover in Greenland is down to human influence but says there is low confidence in finding evidence linking loss of Antarctic ice with human influence.

Unsurprisingly, given the general upward trend in global temperatures, the data reviewed by the IPCC suggests there has been an increase in extreme high temperatures around the world and a decrease in extreme low temperatures. Even so, such is the variability of the climate that low-temperature records continue to be set. Spain (2021), Indonesia (2019), Lebanon (2017), Qatar (2017), Israel (2015), Jordan (2013) and Italy (2013) are among the countries which have recorded their lowest national temperature records within the past decade. Moreover, the US National Snow and Ice Data Center declared that the winter of 2021 was the coldest yet recorded in Antarctica, with an average temperature over six months of minus 60.9 degrees Celsius.[36] In the autumn following the record cold winter of 2021, Antarctica saw some very high temperatures, with the Concordia Station high on the Antarctic plateau recording minus 11.8 degrees Celsius, 38.5 degrees Celsius above the seasonal average. Notably, the latter incident was granted far more coverage than the record cold winter, with the *Guardian*'s environment correspondent asserting, for example, that the Antarctic 'heatwave' was a 'strong signal of the damage humanity is wreaking on the climate'.[37]

With warmer air comes higher air–moisture content – as a general rule air has the capacity to hold 7 percent more moisture for every 1 degree Celsius rise in temperature. Accordingly, the IPCC states that average rainfall over land has 'likely' increased since 1950. Observations, too, record a general rise in heavy rainfall – balanced, necessarily, with an increase in evaporation. However, the rise in heavy rainfall is very uneven. In Europe, for example, most weather stations have detected an increase in the heaviest rainfall events over recent decades. The same is true in the United States but with no detectable trend in Canada. There has been an increase in heavy rainfall in southern and eastern Africa; data is weak elsewhere on the continent. In South America, too, data is weak. In Asia around two thirds of stations show an increase in heavy rainfall. In Australasia there is no one trend in either direction, although northern Australia shows an increase in heavy rainfall and south and east Australia show a decrease. This latter observational evidence flies in the face of hysterical attempts to blame floods in New South Wales in 2021 on climate change, with headlines such as 'First Fires, Then Floods: Climate Extremes Batter Australia'.[38] Actually, anyone taking trouble to read the IPCC's conclusions would, in the case of New South Wales, come to the opposite conclusion: that climate change is bringing a lower risk of extreme rainfall in that location.

In spite of heavier rainfall in many places the available data presented by the IPCC does not appear to show that this has translated into a greater worldwide risk of river flooding. An analysis of 3,500 rivers around the world revealed that 7.1 percent of them saw an increase in maximum annual flow between 1961 and 2005 and 11.9 percent saw a decrease.[39] This, the IPCC report notes, 'is in direct contrast to the global and continental scale intensification of short-duration extreme precipitation'. True, the data is a bit out of date, and there are other kinds of floods, such as surface-water flooding and coastal flooding, but the IPCC report does not offer any data on those, although it says models project a greater risk of flash-flooding in future. Why doesn't heavier rain always cause more river flooding? There are many factors at play. Increased evaporation may mean river levels are lower when the heavier rain strikes. Stronger plant growth associated with higher levels of carbon dioxide in the air may be taking up more water. Fewer areas may be suffering from rapid snow melt. And river flows may be better managed now. Either way, it is certainly hard to build a case to support the idea that the world is experiencing a wave of river flooding due to climate change.

Nor does the geological record support the idea that climate change has unleashed an age of unprecedented, biblical deluge. Where the climatic record has been examined for extreme weather events, such as in the upper Colorado River or the Yellow River, China, it shows that events recorded over the past 100 years have been exceeded many times in the past 2,000 years. In the case of the Yellow River some historical discharges have been estimated at twice as high as those recorded in the era of instrument records. Studies in the European Alps and the Himalayas have shown a frequency of flood just as great throughout the past 2,000 years as in recent history. Studies in the Gulf of Mexico and New England have shown that storms of similar intensity to those measured in recent years have happened multiple times over the past 2,000 years. In Queensland, on the other hand, severe storms have been shown to have been more common in the past than they are now.[40]

As for trends in drought, there are several different ways to measure it: lack of rainfall, low soil moisture, low river flows and low atmospheric moisture. All show a mixed picture. Longer, more intense droughts have been observed in Southern Europe and West Africa. Other areas, such as northern and central Australia, Northern Europe and central North America, have shown a trend towards shorter, less intense droughts. Some parts of the world – East Africa, Western and Central Europe and the Mediterranean – have shown a decrease in soil moisture, while there is no trend in other areas such as eastern and central North America or North East Africa. As regards river flows, there is no evidence of changes in severity of drought in Western, Northern and Central Europe. Measuring atmospheric moisture, there is evidence of 'slightly higher' risk of drought in some areas – western and southern Africa, the Mediterranean and East Asia – and not in others.[41]

As for storms, we have already looked at what the NOAA has to say about them: there is no convincing trend in hurricanes making landfall in the United States. The IPCC adds that there is some evidence of storms slowing down faster as they hit the US coast, resulting in local higher rainfall totals. It adds that there is some evidence that the amount of damage done by hurricanes has increased – although that is less a measure of change in the climate than in the amount of development on the US coast. A hurricane which a century ago might have passed harmlessly over coastal swamp is now liable to take the roofs off a few prime villas and condos. Elsewhere in the world, there is some evidence of stronger but fewer cyclones in the Bay of Bengal and the southern Indian Ocean, and a westward shift in storm tracks in the Northwest Pacific, meaning some places are more affected and others less so. As for Australia, cyclone activity has fallen.[42]

Outside the tropics, the IPCC notes a likely poleward shift in storm activity, meaning, in the northern hemisphere, fewer storms up to around 60 degrees of latitude and more above that line. In the Northwest Pacific there is evidence of an increase in storms up to the year 2000 and a decrease since then. Convective storms? No significant increase in North America; there is limited evidence elsewhere. Tornados? The number is unchanged since the 1970s but they are tending to occur more bunched together on the same day.

Wildfires? 'The world is on fire', according to Greta Thunberg. But not so much in reality. The risk of fires, states the IPCC, has increased in recent years: the 'global burnable area' – the part of the world's land surface where conditions are ideal for wildfires for a large part of the year – has doubled since 1979, and the mean length of the 'fire season' has increased by 19 percent. Yet the total area actually burned by wildfires has trended downwards since the 1990s. Satellite data collected by the NASA Earth Observatory shows that since 2003 the global area being burned annually by wildfires has fallen by a quarter.[43] This is in particular because of a fall in fires on savannah land as farmers use machinery rather than fire to clear land.

In the United States, where nationwide statistics on wildfires have been kept since 1926, there has been a rise in the land affected by wildfires since the 1980s, when an average of 2.97 million acres burned per year. The figures for the past five years (2017 to 2021) are: 10.0, 8.8, 4.7, 10.1 and 7.1 million acres. Yet go back nearly a century and the National Interagency Fire Center (NIFC) records that vastly greater acreages were then being burned: between 1926 and 1943 there was not a single year when the acreage burned dipped below 20 million acres. In 1930 it peaked at 52.3 million acres.[44] From the mid-1940s onwards, though, the acreages being burned dropped markedly. However strong the influence of the climate, it is clear there is a far bigger factor in play: the ability of firefighting services to tackle wildfires and their willingness to do so. As Doug Morton, a forest scientist at NASA's Goddard Space Flight Center puts it, 'climate change has increased fire risk in many regions, but satellite burned area data show that human activity has effectively counterbalanced that climate risk, especially across the global tropics'.[45] Indeed, that is part of the problem behind wildfires now. Before human influence, large areas of woodland were regularly affected by ground fires, which thinned out the wood and cleared the undergrowth. One tree, felled in 1854, was found to have survived 33 fires in its 300-year life. When fire services became better at tacking fires, this natural process was interrupted. As a result, forests grew thicker and dead wood accumulated on the forest floor, so that when, eventually, there is a fire it is liable to be a far bigger fire than those experienced in the past, consuming whole trees rather than just the undergrowth. As Valerie Trouet, professor of dendrochronology at the University of Arizona has put it, North America's forests are suffering from a century of 'fire deficit'.[46]

The story of the NIFC data itself tells an interesting story. Until 2021, the body published data for wildfires going back to 1926. Then, suddenly, all data prior to 1983 was removed on the grounds that it was not collected under 'current reporting processes' (although the data can still be found on archived web pages). It just so happens that the 1970s and 1980s marked a low point in wildfires in the United States, with the result that the only data published by the NIFC covers a period of steadily rising wildfires, missing out the huge fall in fires in the middle of the 20th century. The revision of the data, therefore, just happens to serve the narrative that human-induced climate change is hastening us towards a hellish future of conflagration, ignoring the wider, more complicated picture.

That is a summary of the real-world climatic observations: a firm rise in global temperatures and a very likely overall increase in rainfall, but otherwise a mixed bag of trends and counter-trends, many of them inconvenient to human societies, yet some benign and some beneficial. The IPCC also presents a vision of the future climate, arrived at through numerous attempts to model it. We should be wary of models because they are just that: crude simplifications of complex processes which are not fully understood. But then we have no other way of foretelling the future climate: we can't conduct controlled experiments of the Earth's atmosphere, building two parallel Earths, one with pre-industrial and one with current levels of carbon dioxide. Yet it is so often the models which dominate reporting of IPCC reports, rather than the real-world data. Moreover, it is the extreme scenarios which tend to attract the most attention.

In presenting its modelling of future climate, the IPCC sets up five scenarios.[47] In the first, carbon emissions drop rapidly from the current time, and by 2050 are negative. In the fifth, the world not only carries on burning fossil fuels, but does so at an ever-increasing rate so that by 2050 carbon emissions are more than three times what they are now. The other three are gradations in between. In the lowest case, by 2081–2100, temperatures reach a maximum of between 1.0 and 1.8 degrees Celsius above the level of 1850–1900. In the upper case, they reach between 3.3 and 5.7 degrees Celsius above that level. As noted, the Earth has already experienced 0.99 degrees Celsius of this warming.

The world is certainly nowhere near being on track for the first scenario, but then neither is it on course for the latter. As it happens, global greenhouse gas emissions have increased by approximately 50 percent in the past three decades, from 32.65 billion tonnes carbon dioxide equivalent (CO_2e) in 1990 to 48.94 billion tonnes in 2018 – with falls in many developed countries more than offset by rises in developing countries.[48] If this trend were to continue, global emissions would be half as high again in 2050 as they are now – not three times as high, as the IPCC's worst-case scenario assumes. But so often it is the worst-case scenario which gets reported – and presented as if it is fact.

The IPCC attempts to quantify what it sees as the extreme climatic effects emanating from these temperature rises. At a rise of 1.5 degrees Celsius, it claims, the hottest day of the decade would be 1.9 degrees Celsius hotter than it is now, a long drought would be 2.4 times as likely to occur, heavy rain (equivalent to what a location might now be expected to see once a decade) would be 1.5 times as likely to occur and the proportion of tropical cyclones in the strongest categories (4–5) would rise by 10 percent. If global temperatures reached 4.0 degrees Celsius above 1850–1900 levels the hottest day of the decade would rise by 5.3 degrees Celsius, a drought would be 5.1 times as likely to occur, heavy rain would be 2.8 times as likely and the proportion of the strongest cyclones in categories 4 and 5 would rise by 30 percent. Sea levels would rise by 1.01 metres by 2100 and by 1.88 metres by 2150.

It is not yet easy to judge the accuracy of these models because of the timescale over which climate change happens, but models from the 1980s, looking ahead to the 2020s, have had a poor record – in one prominent case overestimating the level of warming by 50 percent.[49] Other projections which can already be measured against fact have, too, proved wide of the mark. In 2010 the IPCC had to withdraw a claim made in its report three years earlier that the Himalayan glaciers would have melted by 2035 – it had been based on an interview with a scientist in 1999 and was already well out of line with reality.[50] In his 2006 film *An Inconvenient Truth*, Al Gore asserted that the snows on Mount Kilimanjaro would be gone 'within the decade'. While there has been some continued erosion in the mountain's glaciers, they are very much still in existence.[51]

Climate models ought to have got better since those predictions were made – but then again, we won't know how good they are for another 40 years or so. Yet climate policy often seems to treat modelling as fact – as if it produced observations somehow handed down to us from the future. The whole COP26 process operates on the assumption that if a computer model tells you that cutting greenhouse gas emissions to net zero by 2050 will result in a global temperature rise of 1.5 degrees Celsius then that is exactly what will happen. Yet the limitations of modelling are well known. It may appear to produce appealingly precise answers, but models are only as good as the assumptions built into them.

But even if global emissions did rise threefold – which would require the world not just to miss its carbon reduction targets but completely to ignore them – and all these worst-case changes in the climate really did occur, would that really amount to 'climate collapse', 'climate breakdown', 'climate cataclysm' and all the other emotive terms which seem to have displaced plain old 'climate change'?

The IPCC's worst-case scenario – which models such things as a global temperature rise of 4 degrees Celsius, wind speeds in the strongest tropical storms rising by 5 percent and rainfall from tropical storms rising by 12 percent, as well as sea level rises of a metre by 2100 – would present serious challenges in many places, but even that would hardly amount to a 'cataclysm' for human civilisation. We have lived through many ice ages, with rapid warming and cooling of the climate occurring over a few decades. Surely, an advanced industrial civilisation could find ways to cope with all these changes.

The assertion that climate change is an existential threat to human civilisation rests on the conceit that the Earth's climate as it happened to be in the 20th century represented the only environmental conditions in which we can live and thrive. But it is a fair guess that if the climate was currently cooling – as it did slightly between the 1940s and 1970s – we would be worrying about that, too. Indeed, I am old enough to remember in the 1970s warnings about an impending ice age.

It is very easy to spread fear. Make a television documentary in which footage of extreme weather events is overlain with vague statements about climate change, and you sow the idea in viewers' minds that we are headed for a hellish future. There can never have been a time when some part of the world was not in a heatwave, another part was not flooded, another suffering unusually high temperatures and another unusually low temperatures. Yet if you report on every extreme event and throw in the term 'climate change', you will very rapidly plant the idea among your readers that the world is in some freakish transformation.

Of all changes in the climate rising sea levels is perhaps the most serious threat, at least in Britain. A warmer Earth means melting ice and thermal expansion of the oceans. It is an unfortunate fact that vast numbers of people live in cities which are very close to sea level. Even without a warming Earth we would face serious problems in the longer term: sea levels rose dramatically after the last ice age and have continued a slower upward trend ever since. But human-induced climate change will inevitably speed up the process, with global sea levels currently rising at an average of around 3 mm per year.

But doom scenarios in films like *The Day After Tomorrow*, in which cities are suddenly inundated with great waves of water? In spite of much-reported glacial retreat and the calving of some ice shelves, projected sea level rise for the foreseeable future comes nowhere near the levels commonly presented in fiction. In its lowest emissions scenario, the IPCC sees global sea levels rise by between 0.28 metres and 0.55 metres by 2100 and by between 0.37 metres and 0.86 metres by 2150. In the very highest emissions scenario it sees them rising by 0.63–1.01 metres by 2100 and by between 0.98 and 1.88 metres by 2150. It loosely adds that a 5-metre rise by 2150 'cannot be ruled out'. Any of these scenarios would make it harder to defend low-lying cities, but hardly beyond the ability of current technology. Parts of Britain already lie a metre below sea level and are adequately protected. Even in the worst-case scenarios, for the next century at least, and probably well beyond, we will be able to continue to live where we do now, by adopting the drainage and flood defence policies of the Netherlands. There, a quarter of the land surface already lies below sea level and the lowest point is a full 6.7 metres below sea level. Yet flooding is rare because sea defences are strong and because drainage is so well managed. The idea that the world is going to sit by and do nothing as major cities are inundated – as happens in the Hollywood films – is absurd. It is true that some countries in their present state of development would struggle to match the sea defence policies of the Netherlands. But that is all the more reason to ensure that they can continue to develop and become wealthy – rather than undermining economic growth as ill-thought-out climate policies could all too easily do.

None of this is to say that we should not reduce – and indeed try to eliminate at some point – greenhouse gas emissions. But it is to say that many of the statements which are being made to justify the 2050 target are alarmist and in no way supported by evidence. To sum up the evidence reviewed by the IPCC, the Earth is warming, leading to a rise in extreme high temperatures and a fall in the number of extreme low temperatures over most of the globe. The world is also seeing higher rainfall, and heavier, although this is not translating into greater flood risk in most cases. Storm tracks in some parts of the world have shifted, leading to a rise in storms at high latitudes and a fall elsewhere. There is no increase in tropical storms, although they may be dumping more rainfall in some places. Some places are suffering more drought, others are seeing less dry conditions. Fire risk has increased in some places but this has not translated into an overall increase in land affected by wildfires. The effect of climate on fires is dwarfed by the effect of land use.

Yes, it is very much in our interests to burn less fossil fuel, and to decrease greenhouse gas emissions more generally, even to try to eliminate them eventually. But no, we are not being fried, frozen, drowned, burned or blown away by human-induced climate change. That is hyperbole; panic which is being used to suppress debate over net zero and forcing us into making some very poor decisions. The year 2050 is a false deadline for reaching net zero carbon emissions, obsession with which has the potential to do huge damage to our economy and living standards – and, by suppressing wealth and the ability to cope with extreme weather – make us poorer and at far greater risk of natural disaster.

16.

Green jobs

PART OF THE GOVERNMENT'S JUSTIFICATION for setting Britain a unilateral target for eliminating greenhouse gas emissions ahead of most countries is that it will give us a head start in developing new technologies. 'Our green industrial revolution will be powered by the wind turbines of Scotland and the North East,' declared the then Prime Minister, Boris Johnson, launching the government's 'green jobs' strategy in November 2020, 'propelled by the electric vehicles made in the Midlands and advanced by the latest technologies developed in Wales.' All in all, he claimed, the drive for net zero would create 250,000 'highly skilled green jobs' in the UK.

Ah, 'green jobs'. They have been a favourite parrot cry of governments and campaigners over the past few years – in spite of no one really agreeing what a 'green job' is nor what is so special about it. Johnson's contribution was typical: there is a conceit that jobs in renewable energy and such sectors are somehow more valuable, more esteemed than equivalent jobs elsewhere in the energy sector. Get a job installing gas boilers and you are a mere gasman; get one installing heat pumps and you have a highly skilled green job.

But let's not nit-pick. If the drive to net zero really was creating large numbers of well-paid jobs and sparking off a new industrial revolution in Britain that would, of course, be a good thing. But is it? The reality, sadly, follows a long way behind the government's rhetoric. Britain has certainly succeeded in creating 'green jobs' of the regulatory kind: we have armies of bureaucrats drawing up decarbonisation plans for local councils, inspecting things, taxing things and so on. But when it comes to the wealth-creating jobs – those in sectors which actually deliver green energy and the like – we are not doing quite so well. According to the International Renewable Energy Agency there are 12.6 million jobs world-wide in the renewable energy sector. Britain, with 1 percent of the global population, has less than 1 percent of the jobs: 98,000 of them. That hardly amounts to an industrial revolution led by Britain. The country which during the original industrial revolution could quite reasonably claim to be the 'workshop of the world' is not even holding its own among industrial nations. The UK wind industry employs 34,000 people, solar 6,400 and biomass 29,200.[1] What's more, the green economy appears to have shrunk. The turnover of what the ONS defines as the 'low carbon and renewable energy economy' reached a peak of £46.3 billion in 2018 but then fell in 2019 and again to £41.2 billion in 2020 – pretty well back to where it was a decade ago.[2]

So where are all the green jobs? A remarkable number, in common with jobs in traditional manufacturing industries, are in China. The world's most populous country may be a laggard when it comes to cutting carbon emissions, but it has proved remarkably adept at making a living from other countries' efforts to reach their net zero targets. Around two fifths of all global renewable energy jobs – 5.4 million in all – are in China. The country accounts for 62 percent of global employment in the solar sector, 48 percent in wind and 37 percent in hydropower.[3] Seven out of ten of the biggest wind turbine manufacturers are Chinese firms, whose manufacturing is based in that country.[4]

If there ever was a sector where UK industry ought to

be pre-eminent it is in offshore wind. Britain is the world's largest installer of offshore wind turbines. But what about the upstream jobs: developing, designing and making the equipment? According to RenewableUK, the trade body for the industry, only 29 percent of capital spending on UK offshore wind projects is being spent in Britain. We have a couple of factories, in Hull and on the Isle of Wight, manufacturing turbine blades. But the only UK company manufacturing turbine towers closed in 2020 with manufacturing switched to Vietnam. As for the foundations of offshore wind turbines, UK industry ought to have a head start – as it involves transferable skills from the oil and gas industry, in which Britain has decades of experience. One Fife-based company, BiFab, once employed 2,000 people. But that didn't help it win contracts for offshore wind. In 2020 it went bust, its three yards mothballed.[5] It was later bought out of administration, and has won some work.[6] But the foundations for the East Anglia One wind farm, for example, were built in Ireland, Spain and the UAE.

Some would like the UK government to be more protec-tionist, demanding quotas for equipment to be built in Britain. I do not support such measures; UK companies ought to be able to compete with the best in the world. Protecting them from competition would only make them complacent, and would drive up the cost of renewable energy. But UK manu-facturers ought to be able to expect to compete on an equal footing – and that is being made difficult by the net zero commitment. Remember the figures for energy prices paid by UK industry from Chapter 6 of this book? While German factories in 2021 were paying £25.00 per MWh for their electricity, taking taxes into account, French factories were paying £28.74 and UK factories £46.60.

Remember, too, the perverse way in which and UK carbon emissions are calculated for the purposes of the Climate Change Act, including only emissions spewed out physically within the UK, excluding emissions from the manufacture of goods imported from other countries? If your overriding objective is to reduce UK territorial emissions then current industrial policy is a huge success. Build a wind turbine in the North Sea from components made abroad and you provide Britain with a source of low-carbon electricity. Better still, the emissions from manufacturing the kit go onto some other country's carbon account. But of course the Earth's climate gains nothing from exporting our manufacturing industry. On the contrary, wind turbines manufactured in China, or even Germany, are made using electricity that is far more carbon-intensive than if they were made in Britain.

Can Britain succeed in other green technologies where it has failed to dominate in the components for offshore wind? A lot of faith is now being put into car batteries, with the government sinking £100 million into Britishvolt, a start-up that is building a factory on the site of an old coal-fired power station at Blyth, Northumberland. The factory, it is claimed, will create 3,000 jobs and will be manufacturing 300,000 battery packs a year by the end of the 2020s.[7] For the government, a successful battery factory in a former industrial area would be a great coup, enhanced by the imagery of it being built on the site of a fossil fuel plant. Yet in October 2022 Britishvolt was close to entering administration, only being saved by a last-minute intervention from investors after the government refused to stump up yet more money. The warnings had already been sounded on opportunities for UK industry in the car battery business: in November 2021, Johnson Matthey, an established manufacturer of catalytic converters for car exhausts which is looking to invest in new areas as that business presumably declines, announced that it was abandoning its own foray into vehicle batteries on the grounds that the potential returns did not justify further investment. The company's explanation for the abandonment of the venture was that while the market for car batteries is expanding, it is 'rapidly turning into a high-volume, commoditised market' dominated by large-scale, low-cost producers. For that, read low margins. Johnson Matthey has decided instead to concentrate on areas where its capital investment will be better rewarded, such as hydrogen technology and decarbonisation of the chemicals supply chain.[8] Just because one company makes that decision doesn't mean another UK-based company can't succeed, of course, but we should be wary of going back to the 1970s when public money was sucked into propping up the car industry. When governments try to 'pick winners' in which to invest public money they tend to go for highly visible industries which are seen as a matter of national prestige: cars, aeroplanes, etc. These do not necessarily provide the best margins or the greatest opportunities.

There is nothing special about the renewable energy industry. Manufacturing will gravitate towards wherever costs are cheapest. Design and development jobs will congregate wherever expertise is greatest. Being a large customer, and committing yourself unilaterally to reach net zero ahead of any other country, is no guarantee that either form of work will settle on your shores. To attract jobs in renewable energy and related industries the same rules apply as apply to any other industry: you need to be able to offer low taxes, efficient and not-too-onerous regulation, flexible labour markets, an effective legal system which protects intellectual property and suitable sites with functioning infrastructure. Britain scores quite well in a number of these areas, but that does not mean it has any special affinity for green industries. Where Britain has gained a global lead in certain industries, from areas of finance to specialist engineering to video games, it has been because of a combination of factors: the entrepreneurial input of certain individuals, the existence of a critical mass of specialists and an historical comparative advantage. It has not been because the government has produced a jobs strategy. Trying to talk up expectations of 'green jobs' will mean nothing if we can't tackle high energy costs which are driving energy-intensive businesses like steel abroad. And in this the Net Zero Strategy is part of the problem, not the solution.

17.

Tying ourselves in legal knots

WHY, AS A GOVERNMENT, SHOULD you pass a law forcing yourself to achieve something? You could, alternatively, just try to achieve it, without the legal obligation. Even more to the point, why pass a law forcing yourself to achieve something when you have no real idea how you can or will achieve it? It ought to be obvious that by doing so you are inviting individuals, companies and pressure groups to sue you if you fail. But we won't have to wait until 2050 for the lawsuits; they have already arrived. Friends of the Earth and Plan B Earth have already taken the government to court over the legality of a third runway at Heathrow Airport. What's more, although ultimately the case was unsuccessful, the groups scored a victory along the way – indeed it was only thanks to Heathrow Airport Ltd, which owns the airport, that the case was ultimately rejected.

The case centred on the Airports National Policy Statement (ANPS) made by the government in 2018, and which signalled approval for the runway. The campaigners argued that the statement was illegal because it failed to take into account the commitment that the government had made at the Paris summit of 2015 towards reducing carbon emissions. The case was lost at the High Court, but then went to the Court of Appeal, which supported some of the claims. At that stage the government gave up – effectively conceding that it would be illegal to build a third runway. But Heathrow Airport Ltd took the case all the way to the Supreme Court, which in December 2020 overturned the Court of Appeal's decision. The Supreme Court argued that as an international treaty the Paris Agreement had had no force in domestic law; the government was bound only by the Climate Change Act 2008, which at the time demanded only an 80 percent reduction in carbon emissions. The secretary of state for transport, it ruled, had taken that commitment into account.[1]

The result could have been very different had the ANPS been made a year later when the government was bound by its commitment to reduce carbon emissions to net zero by 2050. The government has put itself under a legal obligation to achieve net zero by 2050 but it has no strategy of how it can achieve that while still allowing international aviation to take place. As yet, we know of no satisfactory way in which long-haul flights can be decarbonised – and therefore it is hard to see how any new airport development is compatible with the 2050 target. If we are going to achieve that target on current known technology it is likely that we will have to close airports, not open or expand them.

The Heathrow case was an opening salvo in surely what is already becoming commonplace: environmental activists taking to the courts to challenge any kind of development, using the net zero commitment in order to do so. The Heathrow case is not the only one already to have been launched. In December 2021 a group called the Good Law Project started to fundraise for a class action against the UK government's Net Zero Strategy, claiming that it did not fulfil the obligations on the government under the Climate Change Act. 'While the government has set the grand target of net zero by 2050, it fails to set out how we will actually get there,' it explained in its appeal. 'We believe this is unlawful.' The following month, another group, ClientEarth, filed a similar lawsuit against the government, claiming that government plans 'will not reduce emissions enough to meet its legally binding carbon budgets'.

On the narrow points made by both groups, it is hard to disagree. Indeed, in July 2022 the High Court ruled (in the case brought by the Good Law Project) that the government's Net Zero Strategy 'lacked any quantitative assessment of the contributions expected to be made by individual policies to reductions in emissions'.

The government hasn't explained how it will reach its target of net zero by 2050. It has pre-announced some policies, such as banning new petrol and diesel cars from 2030, but as we have seen that won't achieve net zero emissions, or anything like it. In numerous areas the government has not explained how the target will be met, and for good reason: it has no idea of how it can be done without severely impacting on living standards. The High Court ruling is just the beginning of a legal onslaught which will increasingly lead to policy on climate, energy, transport and many other things being made in the courts rather than by elected parliamentarians. Wider considerations, such as public well-being, will be squashed by environmental concerns. This is the consequence of government passing a law obliging it to reach net zero when it has little idea of how to get there.

The question is: why has the government done this? Governments don't as a rule pass laws compelling them to eradicate poverty, improve school exam results, stop people dying from cancer – desirable though all those objectives would be. They don't do so because they know they would encounter severe difficulties in achieving them, and would consume time and money fighting opportunistic court cases – time and money which would be better spent on health, education and so on. Yet with net zero an entirely different set of rules seems to apply. But why? We don't know how to end all net greenhouse gas emissions any more than we know how to eradicate cancer. So why the legal obligation? Why not just set an aspirational target, as governments do in all other cases, and leave some wriggle room?

The government is not merely making its own life difficult via a legally binding net zero target – it is making life close to impossible for many businesses, too. In March 2022 ClientEarth – again – launched an action against Shell's 13 directors, claiming that they had breached their obligations under the Companies Act by failing to prepare for net zero. It mirrors an action brought by Milieudefensie, the Dutch arm of Friends of the Earth, along with a bevy of other environmental activist groups plus 17,000 Dutch citizens, against the then-named Royal Dutch Shell. In May 2021 it resulted in a Dutch court ruling against the company, with the judge ordering the company to reduce its carbon emissions to 45 percent of its 2019 levels by 2030. The ruling, which relied on the Netherlands being a signatory of the Paris Agreement rather than any specific Dutch law, also applied to the company's supplies and customers.

There are plenty of non-energy companies which can set themselves such targets, but when you are an oil company prospecting for and delivering the gas and oil on which advanced industrial societies rely, and will continue to rely on for many years to come, it is quite a challenge. Targets such as those imposed on Shell can only realistically be achieved by shrinking the business, through demergers or else by selling off oil and gas interests and trying to reinvest the money by diversifying into other industries. But the world still needs oil and gas, and there are still profits to be made by getting it out of the ground. While Milieudefensie celebrated its success and started writing letters to other high-profile listed fossil fuel companies, the law of unintended consequences sprang into action. By the end of 2021, hedge funds were busily feasting on oil and gas assets being disposed of by listed companies under pressure from activist shareholders and well-funded environmental groups prepared to explore every possibility presented by climate targets and laws. The divestment extended to large investment houses, which, according to fund manager Crispin Odey in October 2021, 'are all so keen to get rid of oil assets they're leaving fantastic returns on the table'.[2] His European fund had doubled in value over the course of the year as a result.

By the end of 2021, Royal Dutch Shell no longer existed under that name. Until then it had listed its shares on both London and Amsterdam stock exchanges, but it suddenly ended its Dutch listing and became a purely British company, called plain Shell. Not that this will protect it from opportunistic legal actions on the part of activists – who, as previously mentioned, have already caught up with the company in the British courts.

Environmental campaigners may feel pleased with themselves – as do hedge fund managers picking up oil and gas assets on the cheap. But the downside is that large European oil and gas companies are withdrawing from the business of exploring and utilising new reserves. The cost of this became apparent by late 2021 when the oil and gas industry was struggling to keep pace with demand from a global economy recovering from the Covid-19 pandemic. The problem was compounded in February 2022 when Russia invaded Ukraine and European countries wanted to retaliate with a boycott of Russian oil and gas but found themselves hamstrung by dependency on Russia. Europe was left short of gas, increasingly quantities of which were being imported in liquid form in refrigerated ships.

In the Netherlands, gas production plunged by 55 percent between 2013 and 2018, with the result that in the latter year it became a net gas importer for the first time.[3] Production was due to plunge further with the closure of the Groningen gas field in 2022, although this has been put off for now thanks to the energy crisis following Russia's invasion of Ukraine. Yet 92 percent of Dutch homes are still heated with gas and that is unlikely to change quickly as there is no alternative which is nearly so cheap.[4] The result is growing dependency on foreign gas just at a time when global prices are soaring. Suddenly, trying to force Shell into giving up oil and gas extraction seemed a lot less clever.

There is really only one way that the government can save itself from being dragged through the courts at increasing frequencies over the next three decades as the 2050 target approaches and we struggle to meet it – that is to repeal the clause in the Climate Change Act which imposes a legally binding commitment to reach net zero by 2050. Were it to be reduced to an ambition or aspiration there would be nothing to sue the government for. As it is, Britain is doomed to descend into a kritarchy, where the real political power is held by judges. It is they who will decide whether people will be able to afford to heat their homes, whether our industry will be competitive, whether our economy can grow or not. It won't help the planet, but it will help to export jobs and opportunities to countries which have not burdened themselves with legally binding targets. The only people who will benefit, of course, are the lawyers. Never mind green jobs, net zero will certainly spawn a large number of bewigged jobs.

18.

Loading costs on the poor

'CLIMATE CHANGE HITS THE POOR the hardest,' asserts the World Economic Forum, citing a McKinsey report which itself claims that people in low-income countries have the most to fear from rising temperatures, 'because they often depend on outdoor work, like in agriculture, or rely on natural capital'. It is a received wisdom that is very commonly expressed: we're all going to suffer from climate change, but it is the poor who are really going to be blasted – who face being fried by inhospitably high temperatures, ever-stronger tropical storms and more intense cyclones.

The trouble is, not everyone in the developing world quite shares the enthusiasm for the net zero targets which the rich world is trying to force upon them in the name of helping them. On the contrary, many see their countries at risk of coming worse off not from the effects of climate change but from the efforts designed to stop it. They complain that they are being expected to decarbonise in advance of wealthy countries, damaging economic growth – and the chance to lift many millions out of poverty – in the process.

On the face of it, Western efforts to help the developing world cope with climate change appear generous. In the lead-up to the Paris climate conference in 2015 developed countries agreed that they would try to put up $100 billion a year from 2020 to help developing countries cope with climate change. While they haven't quite delivered all the money yet, prior to the pandemic they appeared to be well on the way: the OECD estimates that $79.6 billion was handed over in 2019.

But the money comes with strings attached. Much of it is specifically earmarked for renewable energy projects, the price of which is that the recipient countries must first agree to close their coal plants. Over five years from 2021 the UK has committed £11.6 billion for international climate finance. Of this, £550 million has been allocated to projects which help developing countries phase out coal and switch to renewables. Under the government's Accelerating Coal Transition programme, developing countries agree to close coal plants so that money can be spent 'repurposing sites for clean energy generation and creating green jobs'.[1] Yes, those green jobs once again.

But as Thiagarajan Jayaraman, an adviser to the Indian government on climate policy, has pointed out, wealthy countries expect developing ones to transition to renewables faster than they themselves seem to be able to manage: 'when developed countries are unable to implement the coal-to-renewables transition, and in effect doing only coal-to-gas, why are they asking developing countries to do this?'[2] As we've seen there are huge problems involved with switching from dependable fossil fuels to intermittent wind and solar. Either it requires backup from a reliable source of energy such as gas – or it requires hugely expensive investment in energy storage. Yet we expect developing countries to brush all this aside and somehow jump straight into the clean energy future that we can't quite yet manage ourselves.

Jayaraman has also spoken of Western environmentalists who expect developing countries to close down polluting factories without worrying about what happens to the people who work there. The whole subject of 'social justice', he argues, has veered away from health, education and all the things which used to concern global development policies – and become fixated on one aim: limiting global temperature rises to 1.5 degrees Celsius. This 'amounts to saying that all problems of injustice are environmental in origin, which is obviously an absurd statement'.

What really drives improvements in health, living standards and social conditions is not the temperature; it is economic growth. And the developing world has enjoyed that in spades over the past two decades. Across Sub-Saharan Africa, GDP per capita has nearly doubled in just two decades, from $1,981 in 2000 to $3,532 in 2018. In South and South East Asia it has more than doubled, from $3,437 in 2000 to $7,649 in 2018.[3] With it, and on just about every measure, the quality of life has improved. The proportion of people in South Asia suffering from undernourishment, according to the UN Food and Agriculture Organization, fell from 19.0 percent in 2001 to 14.5 percent in 2019; in Sub-Saharan Africa it fell from 26.3 percent in 2001 to 20.3 percent in 2019. Life expectancy in Asia rose from 67.8 years in 2001 to 73.6 years in 2019. In Africa it rose from 53.0 years to 63.2 years over the same period.

If global temperatures continue to rise there no doubt will be some places which will suffer: either through more arid conditions or greater flood risk from heavy rainfall events (although as revealed earlier, data from the period 1960–2005 showed an increase in flood risk in only a small percentage of rivers). Other areas which are not cultivable now may become so in the future, or suffer lower flood risk. But climate change will struggle to do as much damage as we would cause by stalling or reversing economic growth in the developing world. No amount of blather about 'green jobs' can change the reality that development needs affordable energy, and that renewable energy in the developing world comes with the same problems as it does in the developed world. The difference is that many developing countries have coal but no gas and for them it is a lot harder to cut carbon emissions.

This hasn't stopped the World Economic Forum (WEF) from advancing what might be called the leapfrogist argument: that developing countries can jump from a situation where many people live without electricity straight to a future of renewables, missing out the dirty, fossil fuel stage of development. 'Adopting renewables provides a larger degree of independence to developing nations, giving them the opportunity to leapfrog the previous energy transitions and jump straight to the third energy transition,' read one paper published as part of the agenda for the WEF's 2020 meeting at Davos.[4]

The WEF has gone further, publishing proposals for a 'Coal Retirement Mechanism' which would provide incentives for developing countries to close down their coal industries. Under the plan, written by Donald Kanak, the chairman of an asset management company, rich-world investors would buy up coal power plants in developing countries on the condition that the money used to purchase them is invested in renewable energy. The coal plants – many of which are fairly new, with India's only an average of 12 years through their expected 30 to 40 year lifespans – would be closed down in 10 to 15 years' time. The investors would be repaid initially through income received over the remaining years of the coal plants' operation. Then, when the plants are closed, Western investors would be rewarded with carbon offsets – tradeable tokens bought, for example, by airline passengers in order to assuage their guilt for being responsible for so many carbon emissions.[5]

The proposal rests on the idea that renewables are cheaper than coal – and that developing countries would realise this if only they could bring themselves to believe it. To back his assertion, Kanak quotes a figure from Lord Stern, the economist who authored a UK government paper on climate change in 2006, claiming that the cost of coal power is really $200 per tonne if you take into account all the environmental damage it does. But this is four times its actual cost.

It isn't hard to spot a slight issue with the Coal Retirement Mechanism (which, it ought to be noted, is not the WEF's official policy). While the Western investors make a handsome return on their money, helped along by carbon credits, the developing country ends up being deprived of a reliable power supply. As already explained earlier in this book, comparisons which show solar and wind power being cheaper than coal and gas omit a vital detail – that in order to sustain an electricity grid based on intermittent renewables you have to add in another cost: that of storing energy or providing some other kind of backup for when the wind is not blowing and the sun is not shining. And the cost of storing energy, even by the most efficient means widely used at present, hydroelectric pumped storage, is at least twice what it costs to generate the electricity in the first place. How does the Coal Retirement Mechanism proposal address this problem? Merely by suggesting that developing countries will need some 'accompanying financing and technical assistance'.

If renewable energy is such a win–win, and really is cheaper than coal, why don't Western investors put their money directly into renewable energy in developing countries? They would make a packet, wouldn't they, without having to shell out to buy all these dirty, outmoded and expensive coal plants? It seems that for the 'enlightened' investors of the WEF the promise of a steady income from carbon offsets and coal-powered electricity is more appealing than gambling on a return from renewable energy plants in developing countries.

The concept of a Coal Retirement Mechanism for the developing world is the latest manifestation of an unappealing tendency which has been evident in the climate movement for the past two decades: where wealthy people in the developed world try to cut their emissions by proxy rather than by changing their own lifestyles. It is a white saviour mentality. While the wealthy expect to keep flying, driving, and heating their swimming pools, they look to the poor to live the lives of environmental purity which they can't quite manage themselves. The whole business of carbon offsetting works on the same principle as indulgences in the medieval church: they help you buy your way out of your environmental sins. The difference is that indulgences, at least, tended to go to good causes: setting up almshouses and the like. In washing their hands of their climatic sins, on the other hand, the cardinals of climate change have come up with ways of keeping the world's poor in relative poverty. No wonder at COP26 India, China and others refused to sign a document committing them to 'phasing out' coal and would only agree to one which promised merely to 'phase down' use of the fuel. If and when renewables really do become cheaper than coal, it won't need a Coal Retirement Mechanism to persuade developing countries to make the switch. But for the foreseeable future, coal is likely to remain a vital part of the power supply to grow developing-world economies. At present, for example, coal accounts for 72 percent of power generated in India and 56 percent of that generated in Indonesia. You can't close that down and expect their economies to prosper, however much we would like them to be able to leapfrog us to a green future.

Why is it that those who profess to be most concerned about climate change so often turn out to have a carbon footprint the size of a Yeti's? The Davos class do not subsist on green energy: 309 private jets flew into airports close to the Swiss resort for the 2019 event. Indeed, the market for private jets is booming. Aviation data provider WingX reported that 470,000 business flights were flown globally in September 2022, up 4 percent on September 2021 and up 16 percent on September 2019.[6] By contrast, the International Civil Aviation Organization reported that between January and August 2022 the number of passengers carried on airlines was still only 80 per cent of its pre-pandemic levels.[7] Somehow, during a period when international travel had become extremely difficult for the masses, the world's super-wealthy were still managing to fly around. One charter company was reported to have ordered 100 new business jets to serve the market.[8] There was little to discourage such investment. While ordinary travellers were being threatened with the prospect of 'frequent flyer' taxes, and were already being made to pay an ultra-long-haul passenger duty of £91 for each flight over 5,500 miles, business aviation seemed to be managing to thrive.

In July 2021 the EU announced plans to tax aviation fuel for the first time. From 2023 the intention is to impose a minimum tax of €10.75 per GJ (approximately €0.38 per litre) on fuel used by passenger aircraft flying between European destinations.[9] Yet bizarrely, in the original draft, seen by Reuters, the tax was not intended to apply to pleasure or business flights. Nor will the proposal apply to jets flying into or out of the EU. As for private jets, so for yachts: from 2023 the EU also plans a tax on ships of over 5,000 gross tonnage. Yachts, however, will be exempt – even though the largest private yachts are three times this weight. According to a think tank, Transport & Environment, the exempt vessels have between them carbon emissions almost as high as those of Denmark.[10]

There are, it is true, some climate campaigners who practise what they preach and lead hairshirt lifestyles. But there are plenty who do not, and who expect, with a brass neck, to be able to offset their own lifestyles through ingenious schemes to reduce the carbon emissions of the poor. The unwillingness to change lifestyles, unsurprisingly, reaches further down the wealth scale. Opinion polls have repeatedly shown that people are full of enthusiasm in general for tackling climate change, but that enthusiasm wanes somewhat when they are asked whether they are prepared to make personal sacrifices to reduce carbon emissions. It fizzles away further still when it comes to people actually being hit with rising bills.

In January 2021, for example, a poll by the UN Development Programme involving 1.2 million people across 50 countries found that 64 percent agreed with the assertion that there is a 'climate emergency'. Britain, along with Italy, had the most concerned populations of all, with 81 percent agreeing with it.[11] A poll held by YouGov and the Cambridge Centre for Public Opinion Research in October 2021 appeared, at first, to confirm the existence of a worried public willing to do what it could to tackle the problem by slashing carbon emissions, with 70 percent agreeing with the statement 'I would be prepared to change my behaviour to help limit climate change', and only 9 percent disagreeing. But when it came down to specifics it was a different story. Asked about the government's ban on new petrol and diesel cars from 2030 support fell to 42 percent, and asked about a meat tax to encourage less consumption only 19 percent expressed their support.[12] A separate YouGov poll asked in more detail about motoring and climate change. The case for higher fuel duty was rejected by 61 percent to 26 percent, while the idea of reducing the number of petrol stations was opposed by 46 percent to 39 percent.[13]

There lies the problem: people are all for tackling climate change in theory, but when it comes to the realisation of how much it will cost them, they go somewhat cool. Will the public really accept net zero plans if it means a diminution in living standards? Not if the *gilets jaunes* protests in France are anything to go by. High fuel prices caused a revolt in Britain in 2000, with the result that no government has felt brave enough to raise fuel duty in real terms ever since.[14] In spite of claims by vegan campaigners there is little sign of Britons changing their diets to cut meat consumption, whether because they think it might help the climate or for any other reason. The National Diet and Nutrition Survey carried out by Public Health England shows 'no significant differences' in the intake of meat in the five years to 2020.[15] A global poll conducted by Ipsos for the World Economic Forum in 2019 found that only 14 percent of people would be prepared to give up flying in order to reduce their carbon emissions if it meant using more expensive and less convenient alternatives. A further 29 percent said they would consider giving up flying only if the alternative was no more expensive and no less convenient; clearly, there is no such alternative option in the case of journeys of more than around 400 miles.[16] There may be many environmentalists excited by the idea of returning to a simpler form of existence, of abandoning consumerism, of redesigning society along the lines of primitive socialism, but it isn't going to wash with the majority of voters.

The most popular proposal in the first YouGov poll quoted above, interestingly, was a frequent flyer tax – which was supported by 49 percent of respondents. Yes, if the public is going to support any measure to curtail lifestyles it is going to be restrictions on the private jets used by Davos Man as he gallivants around the world lecturing us on how the rest of us must make sacrifices to save the planet. If plutocrats are not prepared to give up their private jets they are going to struggle to convince people of lesser wealth to accept constraints and extra costs on their lifestyles.

When it comes to climate change, the normal rules seem to be reversed. Suddenly, among many politicians and policy-makers, it becomes acceptable to have highly regressive taxation. But what will it cost ordinary people? As in the developing world, so in Britain. A depressingly high proportion of the costs of achieving net zero – or trying to achieve net zero – seem destined to fall on people of modest means. Throughout this book we have looked in detail at the multiple layers of costs of the various technologies which we will need to get anywhere close to net zero. So many of them are loaded on people at the bottom end of the income scale.

We have showered the well-off with grants for their electric cars and their wood-fired boilers. Meanwhile, heating and insulation costs will land most heavily on those on the lowest rung of home-ownership: those who have stretched themselves to buy late-19th-century and early-20th-century houses with solid walls – the classic, bog-standard Victorian two-up two-down. Listed properties, on the other hand, are exempt from Energy Performance Certificates and so will presumably be exempt from many of the costs that the government is proposing – so no large bills for the owners of period mansions.

The costs of running an electric car will be highest for those who do not have access to their own home-charger – householders without driveways, in other words. Poorer motorists already are being driven off the roads even before the demise of petrol and diesel cars. Look at London's Ultra Low Emission Zone which places a daily charge of £12.50 on the drivers of diesel cars over 17 years old and most petrol cars over seven years old but which places no charge on the owners of brand-new supercars who arrive every summer to race around the streets of Kensington.

Food, clothing, consumer goods? It is extremely difficult to put any kind of estimate on how net zero will affect the cost of these, as there are too many unknown factors. But two things are for sure: firstly, that taking land out of production and thus depriving ourselves of the facility to grow our own food is not going to bring down prices for UK consumers. Secondly, that higher food prices will fall more heavily on the poor, a greater proportion of whose income is spent on feeding themselves.

Demand on land for biofuels, solar farms and rewilding projects is going to put pressure on agriculture, leading to greater reliance on overseas imports which in turn will make UK consumers more vulnerable to currency swings. Further, the decarbonisation of aircraft and shipping will add to the cost of transporting goods, and so add to prices in the shops.

But let's just look at one part of the cost of decarbonising agriculture: doing without modern fertilisers and pesticides. We can't know exactly what effect that might have on food prices, but as a guide, in 2016, according to marketing research company DJS Research, a weekly basket of 19 organic foods, including apples, bananas, butter, beef, tomatoes and milk, cost 89 percent more than non-organic equivalents – an extra £870 a year.[17] You can argue that they might be better-quality, and many better-off households are happy to pay these prices. But for a family on £31,400 a year (the median household income in 2021), it is a considerable extra sum.[18] We are already seeing, in the Netherlands, the reaction of the public to the government's ill-thought-out plans to decarbonise agriculture. Targets to reduce nitrogen emissions have condemned a third of the country's livestock industry, sparking road blockades from farmers who will lose their livelihoods as a result. That is the kind of dissent we can expect in Britain if the government pushes ahead with its own net zero plans without thinking through the consequences.

Other goods we use in everyday life? If we are going to have to decarbonise all the plastic, the copper, the steel used in everyday items, that, too, is going to leave its own imprint – although what it will add to the costs of everyday life is anyone's guess. Services? If the cost of transport and energy goes up, so, too, does the cost of eating out, going to a hairdresser's, getting old-age care – all of life's essentials. And so it goes on: layer upon layer of extra expense.

The energy price shock in 2022 gave us a foretaste of a

world of scarce and expensive energy. It was not a comfortable sight. Millions feared that they would be unable to keep warm during the winter, or wash, or cook. A mass civil disobedience campaign was launched, urging people simply to stop paying their energy bills. For some commentators, the price shock was vindication of net zero policy, and showed why we need to move away from fossil fuels to green energy even more quickly than we are. But this is a blinkered view. We have always had spikes in oil and gas prices, and by August 2022 the global price of crude oil had yet to reach the levels it had reached in its previous peak in 2008. By October oil prices were falling and wholesale gas prices had crashed to a third of their August peak. What made this spike so painful for UK consumers was that Europe has neglected its fossil fuel infrastructure while still being heavily reliant on it. We have let gas production falter, abandoned gas storage facilities, allowed ourselves to become unnecessarily dependent for the fuel on a belligerent country – Russia. We have also allowed our nuclear industry to decline. If we had a renewable energy industry which was supplying a high proportion of our needs, and which was able to function without backup from gas, we would indeed be insulated from world gas prices. But that is decades away. As already noted, just 4.2 percent of Britain's total energy needs are currently provided by wind and solar and we don't even have the beginnings of an energy storage facility which would allow intermittent wind and solar to become viable as the mainstay of our national grid. We are almost totally reliant on gas to fill the gaps.

And if we were to rush towards an energy infrastructure based on intermittent wind and solar, as the government seems to want to do? We would inflate energy prices even more than the Ukraine crisis has succeeded in doing. We would be paying through the nose to store energy in batteries, hydrogen and other means. And that is assuming we could tap into sufficient wind and solar energy at all – Britain may be a windy country but still there are limits to what renewable energy can be exploited.

Why do so many people happily advocate policies which they must know would impoverish us? For a decade, one of the most-used words in political debate in Britain was 'austerity' – used to attack government policies which prioritised balancing the books. Yet many of the same people who threw about the word 'austerity' now shamelessly advocate climate policies which will make the poor poorer.

'The Green Party is immensely proud to be one of those organisations calling for an end to austerity and for investment in an economy that puts people first,' declared a press release from 2014.[19] Seven years later, Caroline Lucas, the Green Party's only MP, was writing to the *Guardian*, complaining that 'there is a fundamental flaw in Boris Johnson's approach to tackling climate change, and that's the G-word – growth . . . the endless pursuit of economic growth, as the lodestar of government policy, is what is driving the climate crisis.'[20] I don't know what Lucas thinks would be the result if a government were deliberately acting to stifle economic growth, but it would certainly fall under my description of 'austerity' – with knobs on. The Green movement now has a word for what it wants to achieve: 'degrowth'. An alternative way of describing this is 'permanent recession'.

If you point out this inconsistency, the standard response is that we simply have to reach net zero by 2050 (or even earlier) because the costs of delay will be much higher than taking action now – in other words you will have to accept the impoverishment that we will force upon you because even greater impoverishment will be coming your way as a result of climate change. How come? As a result of climate change-induced storms, floods, heatwaves, etc. Except that observational data on the climate doesn't support all these prophecies.

Whatever the climate does throw at us, we will be far better equipped to cope with it if we have a functioning, growing economy rather than one which has been suppressed by zealous efforts to reach the target of net zero by 2050. Should we try to cut carbon emissions? Certainly. But we should start with a golden rule: that in doing so we should not force it at a pace, nor make any decisions, which would compromise economic growth.

19.

So what should we do?

CARBON DIOXIDE IS ACCUMULATING IN the atmosphere; global temperatures are rising by around 0.1 degrees Celsius per decade, and it is highly likely there is a causal link between those two things. We are seeing greater extremes of high temperature. Sea levels are rising by around 3 mm a year. We don't know for sure what will be the effect of changing the composition of the atmosphere, except that it is a risk we might rather avoid. Carbon emissions aside, fossil fuels are polluting. They are concentrated in politically unstable parts of the world and they are in finite supply.

On these things, most people can surely agree. There are many good reasons why we should seek to shift to cleaner forms of energy and to reduce, eliminate even, carbon emissions. But there are other things, too, on which we ought to be able to agree – if the current political climate allowed. No, humans are not heading for Armageddon. We are not going to be driven to extinction as a result of climate change-induced flood, fire and tempest. Observed changes in the climate to date are moderate; bad in some ways but beneficial in others (it's just that unlike more intense heatwaves we don't notice that storms have become a little less powerful and that fewer people have died from the cold). Some claims that climate change is bringing us more extreme weather are genuine – in the case of heatwaves and heavier rainfall in some places. Other claims – such as that climate change is bringing us more terrifying storms, are contradicted by real-life observational data. But even if we accept the IPCC's warnings of greater downsides outweighing any benefits, there is nothing coming that will be beyond our ability to cope. With the exception of Antarctica – although even that now supports scientific communities – humans long ago succeeded in settling every continent on Earth, and with far more basic technology than we have now. The range of human habitation already extends between places which regularly exceed 40 degrees Celsius in summer to places which often sink below minus 40 degrees Celsius in winter. Humans live in places ranging from tropical rainforests to desert, from 1,400 feet below sea level on the shores of the Dead Sea to 18,000 feet above sea level, and in places where the wind regularly exceeds 100 mph. We are not going to be defeated by an upward shift in average temperatures by a degree or two and by an increase in precipitation to the tune of a few percent. To reach net zero by 2050 is an arbitrary target. It is not a deadline which, if we fail to meet it, will result in the Earth's ecosystem collapsing, and human civilisation with it. To argue so is to try to turn climate change into a morality tale, to treat it like something out of the Old Testament. Indeed, the Old Testament – in common with many other religious texts and oral traditions from all over the world – has its own great flood story, in which humans are punished for their sins by a great deluge. The hysterical version of climate change is that same tale, updated for the present.

But if we can accept the general case for cutting and trying eventually to eliminate carbon emissions, how should we go about it? We ought to start with a general principle: that whatever action we take, it should not come at the cost of economic growth. If we do impoverish ourselves, we will put ourselves far more at risk of natural disasters – the very thing from which we are trying to protect ourselves. This is an annual average of deaths globally from natural disasters, by decade, over the past century, compiled by the website Our World in Data. It is worth remembering as you read it that the Earth's population has risen from 1.8 billion in 1920 to 7.8 billion today.

1920s	523,893
1930s	462,798
1940s	386,592
1950s	212,746
1960s	174,043
1970s	98,836
1980s	74,994
1990s	43,359
2000s	78,138
2010s	45,260[1]

That is over a century in which we have supposedly been careering towards climatic Armageddon, in which we are continually served up images of floods, droughts and typhoons, and invited to believe that climate change is already killing millions – and about to kill off billions more. It is a century of rapid population growth, in which human societies have colonised places, more vulnerable to natural disaster, which might have been avoided in earlier times. We have fewer people dying from natural disasters year on year not because the climate is becoming more benign, but because we are becoming wealthier and better able to cope with adverse events. It is wealth which allows us to build stronger buildings better able to withstand storm and flood. It is wealth, too, which allows a low-lying country like the Netherlands to defend its citizens against inundation from the sea while a similarly vulnerable country, Bangladesh, struggles. It is wealth which allows weather warnings to be rapidly circulated among the population, and which allows emergency help to be quickly deployed after the event. Compromise wealth-creation and you compromise that ability to cope.

There are many technologies which could lead us to a cleaner future of lower greenhouse gas emissions and less pollution from soot, nitrogen oxides and so on. Some of them might one day prove to be more economically effective than the technologies they replace. Others will be hidings to nothing, dead ends which fail to deliver their promise. At the moment we don't know which are which. But there are plenty of green technologies which are already failing to live up to the hype surrounding them: press releases announcing ideas of which you hear no more, start-up businesses which quickly crash and burn, initiatives which you wonder were mere PR stunts, designed to convince customers and investors that the company is taking net zero seriously rather than a genuine effort at solving a problem. High-tech ocean-going sailing vessels, wave-power generators which bob up and down on the sea; they are just two ideas currently being touted which bear a striking resemblance to ideas presented in magazines and on the TV programme *Tomorrow's World* back in the 1970s. By its very nature innovation involves a huge number of failures and a few successes. But in setting ourselves an arbitrary date for decarbonising the entire economy – and less than 30 years into the future – we are forcing ourselves to make huge bets on technologies which are destined to fail.

Imagine if we relaxed that target, if we said that we would like to reach net zero by 2050 but that we are not going to tie ourselves down with a legal commitment to do so. The pressure would be off and we would be able to give ourselves – through market mechanisms – time to sort the technological wheat from the chaff. When the right solutions come along, they would not need to be forced upon unwilling households at great expense; they would sell themselves on their own merits. One of the greatest breakthroughs of the past decade, in terms of cutting energy use, hardly ever gets a mention: it is the LED lightbulb. Not only does it use a tenth as much energy as a traditional incandescent lightbulb, it does the job of lighting a house much better: by producing much purer white light – or, if you don't want that, then light of any shade you wish. The LED lightbulb is more expensive, but it lasts much longer; I have replaced only one in four years. In the 1970s I grew up in a household with 12 lightbulbs – which would have consumed 1 kW had we dared turn them all on at once. I have just counted 52 lightbulbs in the house in which I now live; yet between them they would consume only around 250 W if they were all on at once.

LED bulbs are an example of all-round gain. Yet in its rush to try to reduce our energy consumption the EU forced upon us a much less-good alternative. It banned incandescent bulbs half a decade too early, when the only other option was compact fluorescent lamp (CFL) bulbs. Such bulbs can cause problems for people with epilepsy and contain quantities of mercury which are hazardous to the environment and can potentially cause harm to the occupants of a building if the bulbs are broken. And, while they are more efficient than incandescent bulbs, fluorescent bulbs use more energy than do LED bulbs. Forcing them upon the population was a classic example of trying to move too soon, before a far superior technology was ready. Indeed, once LED technology was available there was no need to legislate at all; the market would have done the job of making incandescent bulbs all but extinct.

The mistake over lightbulbs didn't matter a lot because lightbulbs are relatively cheap and short-lasting. It will be much more serious if we make a mistake with electricity generation. For all the serial disappointment, nuclear fusion it is still arguably the most likely technology to fulfil the quest for cleaner energy. It has what renewables lack: energy density. If fusion can be harnessed no one will want to build a large wind farm or solar farm ever again – nor, for that matter, a nuclear fission power station. We won't need to plaster huge areas to capture diffuse rays from the sun; we will have our own little suns which will produce energy at any time of day, while consuming hardly any land.

Yet nuclear fusion is not going to arrive in time for our 2050 deadline. With any luck we might have a fully working power station by then, but not before we will have invested many billions of pounds in wind, solar and associated energy storage. Those who advocate the net zero target like to warn that the oil industry faces a future of 'stranded assets', but the renewables industry, too, will one day be left with stranded assets should nuclear fusion ever realise its promise.

It is one thing for governments to encourage the development of new technology through tax incentives and grants. We can't always rely on private finance, especially if the costs of development are high and the potential rewards lie far in the future. Nuclear fusion has private backers now, but it would probably never have got off the ground had it not been for government money. Why not invest directly in promising technologies – let the taxpayer retain a stake, rather than simply give money away? Tidal power, green hydrogen, nuclear fusion might all have a large role to play in future energy. But it is quite another thing to build entire industries on the back of government subsidy. Wind and solar certainly fall into that category. Some wind and solar farms may operate without subsidy now, but for years these industries were propped up by having the market rigged in their favour.

As things stand, we are painting ourselves into a corner in which we try to rely too heavily on wind and solar energy. I suspect that we will end up trying to resolve the intermittency problem through the use of hydrogen as energy storage – by having solar and wind farms generate large quantities of hydrogen when solar and wind energy is plentiful, to be stored for when it is needed. That certainly seems to be the way the government is heading with its hydrogen strategy. But the costs would have to come down hugely before such a system could give us energy at anything like the price we have enjoyed for the past two centuries. We should be very careful about over-committing to one solution. No more subsidies should be offered for wind and solar farms unless they include sufficient energy storage to provide continuous and predictable power.

We should be diversifying investment in renewables, especially into tidal energy, of which Britain has huge potential. Building a tidal barrage might seem expensive compared with building wind and solar farms, but it promises to be more reliable and less intermittent, thereby saving a lot of money on energy storage (at least if we build a number of tidal power stations around the coast, where the times of the tides vary). Moreover, tidal barrages would provide the estuarine flood defences that we are going to need owing to sea level rise and the sinking tectonic plate on with southeast England sits.

While we await new technologies it is clear that we will need to rely on natural gas. For as long as we are dependent on gas, it would be far better if we derived more of our gas from sources close to home. The North Sea has not been exploited in recent years as much as it could have been; it has been allowed to run down in the belief that the whole gas industry can be decommissioned by 2050, or even 2035. Britain's shale gas reserves remain entirely untapped, as a result of a government moratorium which, for the moment, has brought the industry to a halt. This was in spite of a study by the Royal Society and Royal Academy of Engineering which debunked the myths surrounding fracking and concluded that 'health, safety and environmental risks associated with hydraulic fracking as a means to extract shale gas can be managed effectively in the UK as long as operational best practices are implemented and enforced through regulation'. The risk of water contamination, it concluded, was very low – given that the rocks being fractured were a long distance down from aquifers used for water extraction. The 'earthquakes' reported from fracking were the most minor of tremors, few of which could be felt by humans on the Earth's surface.[2]

Yet the government withdrew support for fracking altogether in 2019 on the basis that 'it is not possible with current technology to accurately predict the probability of tremors associated with fracking'.[3] No one has ever successfully predicted seismic activity; what matters is the risk of harm done when it does occur, which in this case is very low. As the Royal Society report explained, there is nothing new about fracking; it has been conducted for decades in the oil and gas industries. The only relatively new component is its application to shale gas. The government appears to be using what it calls 'earthquakes' – i.e. minor tremors – as an excuse to suppress the industry, to avoid upsetting a powerful anti-fracking lobby. It is siding with irrational fear over scientific evidence – and making Britain much less energy-secure as a result.

Moreover, UK power plants which run on locally produced gas would have lower emissions than those which, as they increasingly do, run on liquefied natural gas (LNG) imported from the United States, Qatar and, until now, Russia. This is because the liquefaction and regasification processes themselves involve significant greenhouse gas emissions. A 2019 study by the US National Energy Technology Laboratory concluded that electricity generated in Europe using LNG imported by ship from the United States would be responsible for 636 kg carbon dioxide equivalent for every MWh generated. Of this, 38 kg came from the liquefaction process,

28 kg from the ocean transport and 4 kg from the regasification process.[4] Transporting gas long distances by pipeline
also increases emissions – the study concluded that the LNG
option would result in fewer emissions than gas imported by
pipeline from Siberia. However, it follows from these figures
that a little over 10 percent of emissions could be avoided
if we ran our power stations on locally produced gas. The
frequently made argument that the creation of a UK shale gas
industry would have had no effect on the surge in wholesale
gas prices in the summer of 2022 because wholesale prices are
set globally is bunk. Locally produced shale gas would always
be cheaper than imported LNG because we wouldn't have
the cost of liquefying it, transporting it thousands of miles
and regasifying it. Moreover, the reason gas prices surged so
high all across Europe was that countries were desperate to
fill their storage tanks before winter, and there were very
limited facilities for receiving LNG. Had UK shale gas been
available, it would have eased the supply problem – and
therefore lowered prices – considerably.

Then there is the issue of food security, which hardly seems
to have entered into the formulation of the policy on net
zero. We have committed huge acreages to solar farms and to
rewilding without any regard to what it means for food
production. The result will be to make Britain more dependent
on imports, and to put consumers at the mercy of interrup-
tion in global trade through war and pandemic. If we are
going to free up some land for rewilding without compro-
mising food security and without forcing everyone to go
vegan we are going to have to look at increasing food production through a great land-intensification of certain types of
farming. In Japan, a densely populated, mountainous country
with even greater land pressures than Britain, a company called
Mirai has found a way of producing green vegetables that is
between 50 and 100 times more land-efficient than traditional

market gardening. It produces 10,000 lettuces a day hydro-ponically, without soil, in an indoor environment.[5] Such methods are, so far, more applicable to salad leaves than, say, to wheat, and it is fair to say that many other attempts at 'vertical farming', as it is often called, have failed to prove economical. But this is a whole area of technology which Britain ought to be investigating. Unfortunately, however, the current rules of net zero do not encourage innovation in agriculture. Rather they encourage the agricultural sector to be offshored – so that food production for UK consumers can go on other countries' carbon budgets, while our own farmland is turned over to trees, trees and more trees.

As for agriculture, so for industry: the current rules for net zero merely encourage the offshoring of emissions – rather than genuine innovation. We are never going to get around this problem until we change the way in which we count carbon emissions. We need to do away with the current method of counting territorial emissions and count instead emissions on a consumption basis.

If I could make just two changes to current policy they would be these: start counting emissions on a consumption basis – and relax the wording of the Climate Change Act so that the attainment of net zero becomes an aspiration rather than a legal commitment. There would be many activists who would squeal at these suggestions, to try to tell us that it would mean the world coming to an end. But the alternative is that we see increasing areas of industry and agriculture hollowed out, to no benefit to the planet – the emissions will simply be transferred (or rather increased) as production is shifted abroad.

While it would be desirable in many ways to reduce and eventually eliminate carbon emissions there is nothing wrong with a climate policy which has adaptation at its heart. Human societies have always had to adapt to climate change, as well as to rising and falling sea levels, and we have far better means to do so now than in the past. Yet we are currently guided by environmental doctrines which hold that there is little we can do about a changing climate other than, Canute-like, to try to stop it changing in the first place. Our adaptation policies are a mess. We keep building homes on floodplains and then, when they flood, we blame climate change. We penny-pinch over river and coastal defences, pleading poverty and throwing our arms up at the power of the sea – overlooking the fact that in the past far poorer societies succeeded in not just abating coastal erosion but in reclaiming land from the sea. The Fens of eastern England – a massive area of what is now productive farming – were once a waste, yet were reclaimed between Roman times and the mid-19th century, a period when sea levels were rising just as they are now.

'In the future, some coastal communities and infrastructure are likely to be unviable in their current form,' concluded the government's Climate Change Committee in a 2018 report. 'Building ever bigger defences to protect all coastal communities in the future would be prohibitively expensive'; not only that, it would 'detract from the coastal landscapes that people treasure'.[6] The report's lead author, Professor Jim Hall, suggested instead a policy of being more 'honest' with coastal communities – i.e. telling them they are doomed – and compensation so that they can be relocated inland.[7]

But how much is 'prohibitively expensive'? The committee estimates that the cost of enacting the existing shoreline management plans around the English coast (which are designed to set coastal defence policy for the next 100 years) at £18 billion to £30 billion. In a footnote, however, it admits that this is at future prices, i.e. allowing for what it guesses inflation will be. Why express it that way, when almost every other government document gives costs of future projects at current prices? At today's prices the estimated cost is

£6.4 billion to £9.2 billion. By comparison, the government is currently spending £100 billion on a single high-speed rail line from London to Birmingham and Manchester. More to the point, energy consumers are collectively paying £4.8 billion every year to subsidise green energy and other social and environmental programmes.[8] So why does the Climate Change Committee think the government should be so mean when it comes to defending coastlines?

The aversion to building sea defences shown by many government advisers is not so much financial as ideological. It has become an axiom of green thinking that we shouldn't try to meddle with nature; we should let natural processes like coastal erosion get on with it, for the good of flora and fauna. Coastal defence policy in Britain now revolves around the doctrine of 'managed retreat' – i.e. letting the sea come in, allowing it to erode cliffs and deliberately breaching floodbanks to allow it to form salt marshes. If people complain that their homes are not being protected, they are told it is the fault of climate change. The Climate Change Committee, indeed, cites coastal erosion as a reason why we need to double down on our efforts to eliminate carbon emissions – as if that were a viable alternative to coastal defence.

I first visited the Norfolk village of Happisburgh in the autumn of 2000, when residents of a clifftop road were already contemplating the loss of their homes. Many had moved there prior to 1993 when the sandy clay cliffs enjoyed the protection of a 1950s wooden revetment running along the beach, parallel to the sea. By 1993, however, the revetment was in poor condition and was removed by North Norfolk District Council, which proposed to replace it with a more substantial concrete sea wall – just like the ones which protect dozens of coastal towns and villages around the British coast. One existing such wall, indeed, ends just a few yards south of Happisburgh. The council was obliged to delay the project, however, while it considered two letters of objection – one from an environmentalist who objected in principle to efforts to interfere with coastal erosion and one from the 'lord of the manor': the owner of a seemingly redundant feudal title who claimed he had the right to compensation for any work done to the beach. By the time the objections had been considered, government policy on the funding of coastal defences had changed – they could not now be built unless the value of the property being immediately defended was worth at least twice as much as the cost of the defence works.

That formula turned out to be a false economy. Since 2000, the cliffs at Happisburgh have retreated at speed – continuing an erosion process that has been going on since the last ice age. Several houses have already disappeared and now the entire village is in danger of following, medieval church and all. The collective sense of helplessness shown by government and local authorities persisted until 2013 when a December storm and tidal surge washed away 10 metres of cliff a few miles up the road at Bacton, leaving the gas terminal there only 15 metres from the cliff edge. Given that Bacton gas terminal handles a third of the UK's output of gas from the North Sea, something had to be done.

It is true that building concrete sea walls is not necessarily the best way of defending the coast. The Norfolk coast is subject to a process called 'longshore drift', where sand is transported along the coast by currents. Sand eroded from cliffs in one place is deposited further along the coast, helping to replenish the beach and slow down erosion. Build a sea wall in one location and, if that is all you do, you can interfere with the drift of material: thus the cost of defending one part of the coast can be to speed up erosion elsewhere.

But there is another way: one which, not altogether unsurprisingly, has been pioneered by the Dutch. If the Netherlands adopted a policy of managed retreat it would mean giving up the quarter of the country which lies below sea level and which has been painstakingly won from the sea through centuries of drainage, dyke-building and pumping. Faced with erosion along a stretch of coast in the south of the country, where the land is at 4.5 metres below sea level, in 2011 the state water ministry constructed its *Zandmotor* ('sand motor') – a peninsula built from 21.5 million cubic metres of sand dredged from out at sea. The idea was that tidal currents would then distribute the sand in both directions along the coast, beefing up the existing beaches. Originally designed to protect the coast for 20 years, subsequent monitoring has suggested that it will last twice that time.[9]

Thanks to the success of that project it has now been copied in Norfolk where, in 2019, 1.5 million cubic metres of sand was dredged from a kilometre out to sea and used to build up the beach in front of the Bacton gas terminal.[10] As in the *Zandmotor*, tidal currents have subsequently distributed the sand along the coast, providing protection to several villages as well. As with the Dutch experiment, it has a projected life of 15–20 years, after which the process can be repeated. The cost was £20 million – not minimal, but a lot less than the value of the gas terminal and other property it protects.

So, yes, we can protect the coast if we want to. We don't have to throw our hands up, say there is nothing we can do and blame climate change for erosion – a process which swallowed a number of villages along the Norfolk coast long before the mass burning of fossil fuels began. It is a question of financial priority. At least with sea defences they have a much more rapid return on investment than do efforts to reduce carbon emissions, the latter of which are not guaranteed to have any return at all, if other countries do not follow suit. And even if the entire world stopped emitting greenhouse gases tomorrow, we would still need to defend the coast.

The same fatalism rules inland flood defence policy. For

years, the government has been trying to scare us about rising sea levels and increased rainfall. In 2009 the Advertising Standards Authority was moved to ban an alarmist TV advert made for the Department of Energy and Climate Change, featuring a father reading a bedtime story to his daughter and showing the world overcome with biblical-scale floods – all, apparently, because we left our TVs on standby. Nearly every case of flooding in the years since has been casually blamed by ministers on man-made climate change, and used to justify urgent measures to slash carbon emissions.

Yet when it comes to flood defence policy the urgency seems to disappear. Never mind a strategy to prepare for climate change; we don't even have a strategy to deal with the climate we already have. It happens almost every time a town or village is flooded in Britain: the church, together with the oldest houses, remain comfortably dry, while modern homes are inundated. Surely, if we are concerned about rising sea levels and heavier rainfall the very first thing we ought to be doing – and which costs absolutely nothing – is to stop building on floodplains. Floodplains are not places which are going to flood at some point in the future due to man-made global warming. There is a very good reason why they are wide, flat and covered with alluvial silt: they have been flooded multiple times in the past. Medieval builders seemed to know how to avoid them – and unlike us they didn't have the advantage of digital mapping which can survey the ground and calibrate it with the risk of flooding: whether it be a one-in-100-year event, one-in-200-year event, etc.

Yet in spite of having this information, we continue to build on floodplains: a process which not merely condemns those buildings to flood, but which by obstructing the flow of floodwaters can create problems for buildings which previously stood out of danger. The think tank Localis analysed planning documents from the 12 local authority districts in England with the highest flood risk. In the first nine months of 2021 alone, it found, these authorities had between them granted planning permission for 5,283 homes in flood-prone areas, 4,255 of them in locations where flooding was 'highly likely' – i.e. more than once a century.[11] The fault was partly the result of the councils themselves but partly thanks to central government targets: housebuilding quotas were forced upon councils regardless of their geography. In South Holland, Lincolnshire, for example, 34 percent of the land in the district is classified as high flood risk. Why force development in unsuitable areas when there are surrounding districts with much more suitable development land? Even more to the point, why do it at a time when you are lecturing, at COP26, that climate change has put human civilisation at 'a minute to midnight'?

It is one thing to avoid building in flood-prone areas, but there is a legacy of building on floodplains going back to the 19th century. There are five million homes in England which lie in flood-risk areas; communities which cannot easily be shifted onto higher land. But there are means of defending places in flood-risk areas. We can build flood walls and manage river flow better by holding floodwaters in upstream areas from which they can be released slowly. We can build tidal barriers designed to keep sea water out of the lower reaches of rivers, and so leave more room for river water or even by diverting rivers altogether. We can stop paving over so much land, and start using porous materials when we do want to create areas of hardstanding – a measure which could have averted the worst of the surface flooding experienced in London during the summer of 2021. I am not sure of the provenance of some of the estimates for how much garden area has been lost in London in recent years – it has sometimes been quoted at 22 Hyde Parks' worth, or 5,000 football pitches – but you don't have to wander around suburban London for long to realise that large numbers of gardens have been paved over for parking, helping to speed the flow of rainwater into drains which can no longer cope. But of course, as with all flooding events now, the blame for the 2021 flash floods in London was put fairly and squarely on climate change.

Or we can use a combination of these measures. Following a 1968 flood in the town of Tonbridge, Kent, for example, a dam was built upstream to allow floodwaters to be held back in an undeveloped part of the Medway valley. Since that was built, however, flood defence policy in Britain has turned away from big engineering projects. The Environment Agency, formed in 1996 from a merger of the old National Rivers Authority with various pollution and waste bodies, was set up with an ethos of working with nature. It has been led at various times by an ornithologist, a maths teacher, a diplomat, a professor of environmental studies – but only once, briefly, by an engineer: Sir Philip Dilley, who served as chairman for 15 months after the scandal of the flooding of the Somerset Levels in 2014. The agency had at first refused to admit that those floods had anything to do with the failure to dredge the River Parrett, preferring to blame climate change. Then, photographs started to emerge from the 1960s when the river was dredged regularly and, as a result, was significantly wider. The river was eventually dredged and serious floods have not happened since.

But that was a rare victory for engineering over ecology. More often, the Environment Agency is pursuing schemes like that in Finchingfield, Essex, where in 2019 beavers were re-introduced into the landscape after a 400-year gap in the hope that they would build little dams which act as a natural flood defence by holding water upstream for longer.[12] Of course beavers are admirable animals and it is a good thing to work with nature, but when you hear of flood defence policy being contracted out to furry animals you really have to wonder how committed the Environment Agency is to defending homes and property.

Typifying the current attitude towards flood defence, Hannah Cloke, professor of hydrology at the University of Reading, wrote at the time of the 2014 floods: 'It's hard for politicians to accept their powerlessness, but we must face up to some unpalatable facts. We are likely to see more extreme weather and more floods . . . In the face of a pattern of some of the highest persistent rainfall on record this winter, the Environment Agency could have spent its entire national budget – dredging, landscaping and rebuilding Somerset from the ground up – and the Levels would still have been submerged.'[13] In other words: give up, get out – there's nothing we can do except cower before climate change.

Yet near where I live in Cambridgeshire the land lies even lower than on the Somerset Levels. Indeed, it includes the lowest point in England: 9 feet below mean sea level. But it never floods. Why not? Because the whole landscape is man-made, reclaimed from fenland in the 17th century under the masterplan of Dutch engineer Cornelius Vermuyden – all at a time when the country was vastly poorer than it is now. Rivers were straightened and diverted, new drainage channels built, windmills and later pumping stations constructed to raise water from the lowest ditches. Two 23-mile-long parallel rivers were dug between Earith, Cambridgeshire, and Denver, Norfolk, to divert water from the sinuous Ouse, the half-mile-wide strip between them designed to flood every winter in order that the rest of the fens be spared.

The whole system still works today, in spite of much of the land having sunk in the intervening centuries. So yes, we can keep low-lying places free of floods if we want to – in spite of gradually rising seas and slightly heavier rainfall. It is just that we choose not to. For years, while the government was wasting money on silly TV adverts showing us disappearing beneath the waves, it was allocating a flood defence budget that was truly pathetic: less than £1 billion a year for maintenance of all river and coastal defences in England, as well as the construction of new ones. The budget has been increased since: £2.6 billion was invested in new defences between 2015 and 2020, and the budget for 2021 to 2026 has been doubled to £5.2 billion.[14] But we still lack the capacity to think big. There is no reason, for example, why York – one of the most regularly flooded cities in Britain – should not be granted the same treatment as the Spanish city of Seville where, following serious flooding in 1963, the Guadalquivir river was diverted around the city. The city has not seen serious flooding since.

As we approach 2050, unless there is some miracle advance in technology in the interim, there is going to be intense pressure to relax the legal obligation to achieve net zero by 2050. There are two ways in which the UK government could respond: either by being honest, admitting that it is not practical to achieve net zero by 2050 without causing serious harm to the economy and living standards of the people, and relaxing the target – or by trying to fudge it. As we have seen, the government is already engaged in a giant piece of fudge: by counting only territorial emissions in the UK's carbon emissions figures. This is already doing harm to energy-intensive industries as the government has given itself a perverse incentive to drive those industries abroad so that their emissions count towards someone else's national total.

What would a sensible decarbonisation target look like? First, take away the legal obligation. It is foolish to compel yourself to achieve something when you have no idea as to how you will achieve it, nor at what cost. That should be obvious. Instead, the government should say, as other countries around the world have done: we will try to achieve net zero emissions by 2050, or some date soon after, but we will not do so in a way which will harm economic growth. Would climate activists wail if the government watered down the legally binding target? You bet they would. But the government can offer something in return: it can say that in future all carbon emissions figures and targets will be calculated on a consumption basis – i.e. including emissions spewed out elsewhere in the world in the name of producing products and services for UK consumers, and excluding emissions made within Britain where those emissions are in the cause of manufacturing goods for export. We would then have honest targets, far harder to fiddle.

Above all else, we should stop panicking. At the moment we are responding to modelled, worst-case scenarios and to assertions of climatic doom which have no scientific basis, only an emotional one. We have somehow developed an atmosphere in which anyone who expresses scepticism about any doom-ridden forecast is denounced as a 'denier', yet baseless narratives of doom are promoted as fact. To have succeeded in creating this atmosphere is an astonishing achievement on the part of climate activists. Their manipulation of public emotion is truly remarkable. But any calm reading of real-world climatic observations shows their alarmism to be misplaced. Somehow, government and Parliament must start to tell us the honest story, not adopt the language of the activists in telling us we are 'a minute from midnight' and so on. Such prophecies have already turned out to be wide of the mark – I have lost count of the number of times I have been told that we have 'only five years to save the planet' and so on. It is certainly two decades since I first heard that assertion, and guess what? We are still here, unroasted, unstarved and undrowned. Or take the Pentagon report unearthed by the *Observer* in 2004 which claimed that by 2007 large parts of the Netherlands would have been rendered uninhabitable by flooding and that by 2020 Britain would have a 'Siberian climate' as the system of atmospheric circulation broke down.[15] That was supposed to be a serious attempt to prepare the United States and the world for the consequences of climate change.

Panic is a sure way to make bad decisions. By allowing ourselves to panic, we will invest in the wrong things, make ourselves needlessly poorer and give other, far more polluting countries an economic advantage – likely increasing overall emissions as a result. There are technologies which may one day allow us to eliminate carbon emissions at reasonable cost, but we do not yet know which ones. We will only find out if we allow technologies to prove themselves or fail. The market can play a huge part in coming up with solutions, but to think that it will come up with all the answers just because we set an arbitrary target is foolish. Targets are often helpful in achieving results, but not if they are entirely impractical. We could set a target, say, to eliminate world hunger by next Tuesday – but we wouldn't get there, however much we tried to threaten the bosses of the world's food businesses if they failed. All we would really achieve would be to incentivise officials to cheat the figures – and encourage activists to sue governments and businesses when the target was missed.

All this said, we need to think much more about adaptation of human societies – not just because of man-made climate change but because of natural changes in our environment. Our societies are based too much on the assumption that we live in an unchanging world with a static climate. We buy, sell, cultivate and develop land on the basis that it will always be there – hence so many of us live in immovable, poorly protected cities at or close to sea level, in places which are always going to be vulnerable to change. And yet, we ought to know the risks of this. Man-made influence or no man-made influence it is perfectly clear that the climate has frequently swung between warm and frozen periods in the past, not on time-scales of millions of years but often with rapid changes over periods of decades. Research into the last ice age in North America suggests that it ended over a period of just 100 years[16] – a far more dramatic change than we have seen in the climate over the past century, and all without significant human input. Either we need to invest in adaptation, employing serious engineering, or we need to find some way of making societies more flexible, more transportable. This is not just because of global warming; we would have to do it anyway. Man-made climatic influences may in some ways compound natural processes, but they didn't start sea level rise or coastal erosion. Neither did lethal storms, intense rainfall and deadly heatwaves begin with man-made climate change; they have always been part of what nature throws at us.

By the year 2050 I am sure we will be enjoying the benefits of cleaner energy than we have now. We may even have cheaper energy than we have now. But will Britain or the world have achieved net zero emissions by then? I don't think anyone can possibly know, although I suspect we won't be there. I have a strong belief, though, that given the choice between achieving net zero and maintaining economic growth we will ultimately choose the latter – much to the disappointment of many green campaigners who seem to be motivated by a bizarre desire to halt economic growth. Meanwhile, the sun will still shine, the wind will still blow, the rain will still fall, the Earth will still be very much habitable – and we will look back to the prophecies of climatic doom being made today in the same way that we now look back at Malthus's predictions of mass famine, or indeed the warnings in the 1960s and 1970s that a new ice age was on its way. It is the way with human civilisations: we are programmed forever to worry, to believe that a sticky end lies just around the corner – but we are also imbided with an ability to adapt, to survive and to thrive.

Notes

1. The conference of idle promises

1　Natalia Tilinina et al., 'Comparing cyclone life cycle characteristics and their interannual variability in different reanalyses', *Journal of Climate* 26:17, 2021, 6419–38, doi. org/10.1175/JCLI-D-12-00777.1.

2　*Biodiversity Action Plan*, Network Rail, 2020. Available at www. networkrail.co.uk/wp-content/uploads/2020/12/Network-Rail-Biodiversity-Action-Plan.pdf.

3　'Private jets: Can the super-rich supercharge zero-emission aviation?', Transport & Environment, 27 May 2021, www. transportenvironment.org/discover/private-jets-can-the-super-rich-supercharge-zero-emission-aviation.

4　'Global CO2 emissions rebounded to their highest level in history in 2021', International Energy Agency (IEA) press release, 8 March 2022, www.iea.org/news/global-co2-emissions-rebounded-to-their-highest-level-in-history-in-2021.

5　Daniel Keane, '"Heat apocalypse" warning in France as wildfires spread', *Evening Standard*, 18 July 2022, www.standard.co.uk/news/world/europe-heatwave-heat-apocalypse-warning-france-wildfires-b1013103.html.

6　'UK heatwave: Wildfire left garden like Armageddon – Norfolk renters', BBC News, 20 July 2022, www.bbc.com/news/av/uk-62244872.

7   Sunil Kataria and Mayank Bhardwaj, '"Planet is dying", India's 8-year-old climate crusader warns', Reuters, 28 September 2020, www.reuters.com/article/us-climate-change-youth-india-idUSKBN26J0ZH.

8   Ilona Amos, 'COP26: Climate change will see 320 million people worldwide facing starvation this decade, report warns', *Scotsman*, 8 November 2021, www.scotsman.com/news/environment/cop26-climate-change-will-see-320-million-people-worldwide-facing-starvation-this-decade-report-warns-3449974.

2. Self-sacrifice

1   *The Andrew Marr Show*, BBC, 16 May 2021.

2   *2020 Future Energy Scenarios: Costing the Energy Sector*, National Grid ESO, November 2020.

3   'High Speed 2 costs', Institute for Government, 29 January 2020.

4   Christopher McKeon, 'All Tory leadership candidates confirm commitment to net zero', *Evening Standard*, 18 July 2022, www.standard.co.uk/news/uk/kemi-badenoch-caroline-lucas-alok-sharma-liz-truss-prime-minister-b1013144.html.

3. Meanwhile, in China

1   'Rapid attribution of heavy rainfall events leading to the severe flooding in Western Europe during July 2021', World Weather Attribution, 23 August 2021. Available at www.worldweatherattribution.org/wp-content/uploads/Scientific-report-Western-Europe-floods-2021-attribution.pdf.

2   'Indicator assessment: Mean precipitation', European Environment Agency, 18 November 2021.

3   Beijing Newsroom and Tony Munroe, 'Death toll from floods in China's Henan province rises to 302', Reuters, 2 August

2021, www.reuters.com/world/china/death-toll-flooding-chinas-henan-province-rises-302-2021-08-02.

4 Long Yang et al., 'Typhoon Nina and the August 1975 flood over central China', *Journal of Hydrometeorology* 18:2, 2017, 451–72.

5 Nectar Gan and Jessie Yeung, '"Once in a thousand years" rains devastated central China, but there is little talk of climate change', CNN, 23 July 2021, edition.cnn.com/2021/07/23/china/china-flood-climate-change-mic-intl-hnk/index.html.

6 www.cma.gov.cn.

7 'Country rankings', International Renewable Energy Agency (IRENA), www.irena.org/statistics/view-data-by-topic/capacity-and-generation/country-rankings.

8 'Outline of the People's Republic of China 14th Five-Year Plan for National Economic and Social Development and Long-Range Objectives for 2035, translated by the Center for Security and Energy Technology'.

9 Vincent Ni, 'Low-carbon ambitions must not interfere with "normal life", says Xi Jinping', *Guardian*, 26 January 2022, www.theguardian.com/world/2022/jan/26/xi-jinping-warns-chinas-low-carbon-ambitions-must-not-interfere-with-normal-life.

4. And Russia . . .

1 static.government.ru/media/files/ADKkCzp3fWO32e2yA0BhtIpyzWfHaiUa.pdf.

2 *Gas 2020*, IEA. Available at iea.blob.core.windows.net/assets/555b268e-5dff-4471-ac1d-9d6bfc71a9dd/Gas_2020.pdf.

3 Ibid.

4 Lauri Myllyvirta et al., 'Financing Putin's war: Fossil fuel imports from Russia in the first 100 days of the invasion', Centre for Research on Energy and Clean Air, June 2022, energyandcleanair.org/publication/russian-fossil-exports-first-100-days.

5 *Digest of UK Energy Statistics: Annual Data for UK, 2020*, Department for Business, Energy and Industrial Strategy (BEIS), July 2021. Available at assets.publishing.service.gov.uk/government/uploads/system/uploads/attachment_data/file/1060151/DUKES_2021_Chapters_1_to_7.pdf.
6 'Shale gas in the UK', British Geographical Society, 2022, www.bgs.ac.uk/geology-projects/shale-gas/shale-gas-in-the-uk.
7 *Shale Gas Extraction in the UK: A Review of Hydraulic Fracturing*, Royal Society and Royal Academy of Engineering, June 2012. Available at royalsociety.org/-/media/policy/projects/shale-gas-extraction/2012-06-28-shale-gas.pdf.
8 *Gasland* (2010), dir. by Josh Fox; *Shale Gas Extraction in the UK*.
9 *Shale Gas Extraction in the UK*.
10 'Innovation: Using less energy to liquefy gas', TotalEnergies/CNBC, 8 October 2018, www.cnbc.com/advertorial/2018/10/08/innovation-using-less-energy-to-liquefy-natural-gas.html.

5. An example not being followed

1 'Net Zero scorecard', Energy & Climate Intelligence Unit, eciu.net/netzerotracker.
2 'Net-Zero tracker', Climate Watch, www.climatewatchdata.org/net-zero-tracker.
3 static.government.ru/media/files/ADKkCzp3fWO32e2yA0BhtIpyzWfHaiUa.pdf.
4 'ICOS measurements show huge methane peaks in the atmosphere after Nord Stream leak', Integrated Carbon Observation System press release, 30 September 2022, www.icos-cp.eu/event/1221.
5 *Global Energy Review: CO2 Emissions in 2021*, IEA. Available at iea.blob.core.windows.net/assets/c3086240-732b-4f6a-89d7-db01be018f5e/GlobalEnergyReviewCO2Emissionsin2021.pdf.

6 *Global Carbon Budget 2021*, Global Carbon Project. Available at globalcarbonproject.org/carbonbudget/21/files/GCP_CarbonBudget_2021.pdf.
7 *Global Energy Review 2021*, IEA. Available at iea.blob.core.windows.net/assets/d0031107-401d-4a2f-a48b-9eed19457335/GlobalEnergyReview2021.pdf.
8 Aime Williams, 'US Senate passes Joe Biden's flagship economic package', *Financial Times*, 7 August 2022.

6. Exporting our emissions . . .

1 'UK's carbon footprint 1997–2018', Department for Environment, Food & Rural Affairs (DEFRA); and 'Final UK greenhouse gas emissions national statistics: 1990 to 2019', BEIS.
2 'Manufacturing: statistics and policy', House of Commons briefing paper, 10 January 2020, researchbriefings.files.parliament.uk/documents/SN01942/SN01942.pdf.
3 World Steel Association, via tradingeconomics.com.
4 'Closing the gap: How competitive electricity prices can build a sustainable low-carbon steel sector', UK Steel, February 2021.
5 Ibid.

7. Power . . . at times

1 *Digest of UK Energy Statistics: Annual Data for UK, 2020*.
2 *Digest of UK Energy Statistics: Annual Data for UK, 2021*, BEIS, July 2022. Available at assets.publishing.service.gov.uk/government/uploads/system/uploads/attachment_data/file/1094629/DUKES_2022.pdf.
3 *Digest of UK Energy Statistics: Annual Data for UK, 2020*.
4 *Digest of UK Energy Statistics: Annual Data for UK, 2021*.
5 'Greenhouse gas emissions from burning US-sourced woody biomass in the EU and UK', Chatham House, 2021, www.

chathamhouse.org/sites/default/files/2021-10/2021-10-14-
woody-biomass-us-eu-uk-summary.pdf.

6 John Sterman, Lori Siegel and Juliette Rooney-
Varga, 'Does replacing coal with wood lower CO2
emissions? Dynamic lifecycle analysis of wood bioenergy',
Environmental Research Letters 13:1, 2018, iopscience.iop.org/
article/10.1088/1748-9326/aaa512/pdf.

7 *The Potential Air Quality Impacts from Biomass Combustion*, Air
Quality Expert Group, 2017. Available at uk-air.defra.gov.
uk/assets/documents/reports/cat11/1708081027_170807_
AQEG_Biomass_report.pdf.

8 *Digest of UK Energy Statistics: Annual Data for UK, 2020.*

9 Gill Plimmer, 'Renewables projects face 10-year wait to
connect to electricity grid', *Financial Times*, 8 May 2022.

10 David J. C. MacKay, *Sustainable Energy – Without the Hot Air*
(Cambridge, 2009).

11 Daniel Coles et al., 'A review of the UK and British Channel
Islands practical tidal stream energy resource', *Proceedings of the
Royal Society A* 477:2255, 2021.

12 Simon Evans, 'Analysis: Record-low price for UK offshore
wind is nine times cheaper than gas', Carbon Brief, 8 July
2022, www.carbonbrief.org/analysis-record-low-price-for-uk-
offshore-wind-is-four-times-cheaper-than-gas.

13 www.nordpoolgroup.com.

14 *Projected Costs of Generating Electricity*, IEA, 2020. Available at
iea.blob.core.windows.net/assets/ae17da3d-e8a5-4163-a3ec-
2e6fb0b5677d/Projected-Costs-of-Generating-Electricity-
2020.pdf.

15 *Net Zero by 2050: A Roadmap for the Global Energy Sector*,
IEA, May 2021. Available at iea.blob.core.windows.net/assets/
deebef5d-0c34-4539-9d0c-10b13d840027/NetZeroby2050-
ARoadmapfortheGlobalEnergySector_CORR.pdf.

16 *Digest of UK Energy Statistics: Annual Data for UK, 2021.*

17 grid.iamkate.com.

18 Nathalie Thomas, 'UK peak power prices rise to second highest level since 2018', *Financial Times*, 15 November 2021.

19 *Drax Electric Insights Quarterly – Q4 2020*, Drax Group/ Imperial Consultants. Available at reports.electricinsights. co.uk/wp-content/uploads/2021/02/Drax-Electric-Insights-Q4-2020-Report.pdf.

20 *2020 Grid Energy Storage Technology Cost and Performance Assessment*, US Department of Energy, December 2020. Available at www.pnnl.gov/sites/default/files/media/file/ Final%20-%20ESGC%20Cost%20Performance%20 Report%2012-11-2020.pdf.

21 ukesr.supergenstorage.org/chapters/energy-storage.

22 *Victorian Big Battery Fire, July 30, 2021: Report of Technical Findings*, Fisher Engineering, Inc., 25 January 2022. Available at victorianbigbattery.com.au/wp-content/uploads/2022/01/ VBB-Fire-Independent-Report-of-Technical-Findings.pdf.

23 Andrew Lee, 'Floating wind-to-hydrogen plan to heat millions of UK homes', *Recharge*, 13 September 2019, www. rechargenews.com/wind/floating-wind-to-hydrogen-plan-to-heat-millions-of-uk-homes/2-1-670960.

24 'World's first offshore hydrogen storage concept developed by Tractebel and partners', Tractebel, 17 December 2021, tractebel-engie.com/en/news/2021/world-s-first-offshore-hydrogen-storage-concept-developed-by-tractebel-and-partners.

25 'Energy storage cost and performance database', Pacific Northwest National Laboratory, December 2021, www.pnnl. gov/ESGC-cost-performance.

26 xlinks.co.

27 Waqquas Bukhsh, Callum MacIver and Keith Bell, 'Assessing the value of increasing GB interconnection', University of Strathclyde conference paper, 2020, pure.strath.ac.uk/ws/ portalfiles/portal/106653973/Bukhsh_etal_EPSR_2020_ Assessing_the_value_of_increasing_GB_interconnection.pdf.

28 Daniel Boffey, 'France threatens to cut UK and Jersey energy supply in fishing row', *Guardian*, 5 October 2021, www.theguardian.com/world/2021/oct/05/france-uk-jersey-eu-energy-supply-fishing-row-channel.

29 Howard Mustoe, 'Cross-Channel power cable backed by Tory donor blocked by Kwasi Kwarteng', *Daily Telegraph*, 20 January 2022.

30 Sara Peach, 'What's the carbon footprint of a wind turbine?', Yale Climate Connections, 30 June 2021, yaleclimateconnections.org/2021/06/whats-the-carbon-footprint-of-a-wind-turbine.

31 *Climate Change 2021: The Physical Science Basis – Sixth Assessment Report of the IPCC*, Chapter 11, International Panel on Climate Change. Available at www.ipcc.ch/report/ar6/wg1/downloads/report/IPCC_AR6_WGI_FullReport.pdf.

32 Lee Miller and Axel Kleidon, 'Wind speed reductions by large-scale wind turbine deployments lower turbine efficiencies and set low generation limits', *Proceedings of the National Academy of Sciences of the United States of America* 113:48, 2016, 13570–75.

33 *Severn Tidal Power Feasibility Study: Conclusions and Summary Report*, Department of Energy and Climate Change, October 2010. Available at assets.publishing.service.gov.uk/government/uploads/system/uploads/attachment_data/file/50064/1._Feasibility_Study_Conclusions_and_Summary_Report_-_15_Oct.pdf.

34 www.emec.org.uk.

35 '"Most powerful" tidal turbine starts generating electricity off Orkney', BBC News, 28 July 2021, www.bbc.com/news/uk-scotland-north-east-orkney-shetland-57991351.

8. Nuclear

1 Jonathan Amos, 'Major breakthrough on nuclear fusion energy', BBC News, 9 February 2022, www.bbc.com/news/science-environment-60312633.

2 Ian Chapman, Royal Society Lecture 2019.
3 *International Status and Prospects for Nuclear Power 2021*, International Atomic Energy Agency. Available at www.iaea. org/sites/default/files/gc/gc65-inf6.pdf.
4 *Nuclear Power: Tracking Report*, IEA, November 2021.
5 Ibid.

9. Homes and heating

1 *The Sixth Carbon Budget: The UK's Path to Net Zero*, Climate Change Committee, December 2020. Available at www.theccc. org.uk/wp-content/uploads/2020/12/The-Sixth-Carbon-Budget-The-UKs-path-to-Net-Zero.pdf.
2 *Heat and Buildings Strategy*, BEIS, October 2021. Available at www.gov.uk/government/publications/heat-and-buildings-strategy.
3 *Net Zero: The UK's Contribution to Stopping Global Warming*, Climate Change Committee, May 2019. Available at www. theccc.org.uk/publication/net-zero-the-uks-contribution-to-stopping-global-warming.
4 energysavingtrust.org.uk, November 2021.
5 'Energy efficiency of housing in England and Wales: 2021', Office for National Statistics (ONS), November 2021.
6 Jo Alsop, 'Focus on high temperature heat pumps', The Heating Hub, 22 November 2020, www.theheatinghub.co.uk/articles/high-temperature-heat-pumps.
7 *Net Zero Strategy: Build Back Greener*, BEIS, October 2021. Available at assets.publishing.service.gov.uk/government/uploads/system/uploads/attachment_data/file/1033990/net-zero-strategy-beis.pdf.
8 Will Kirkman, 'Running a heat pump hits £1,251 – 27pc more than a boiler', *Daily Telegraph*, 11 February 2022.
9 *Achieving Net Zero: Follow Up*, House of Commons Public Accounts Committee report, 2 March 2022. Available

at publications.parliament.uk/pa/cm5802/cmselect/cmpubacc/642/report.html.

10 *The Heat Is On: Heat Pump Field Trials, Phase 2*, Energy Saving Trust, 2013. Available at www.energysavingtrust.org.uk/sites/default/files/reports/TheHeatisOnweb(1).pdf.

11 John Humphrys, 'My heat pump has me left in the cold . . . but I'm VERY hot and bothered about the PM's eco-jollity', *Daily Mail*, 22 October 2021, www.dailymail.co.uk/debate/article-10121865/JOHN-HUMPHRYS-heat-pump-left-cold-Im-hot-bothered-PM.html.

12 'UK government launches plan for a world-leading hydrogen economy', BEIS press release, 17 August 2021, www.gov.uk/government/news/uk-government-launches-plan-for-a-world-leading-hydrogen-economy.

13 Ulf Bossel and Baldur Eliasson, *Energy and the Hydrogen Economy*. Available at afdc.energy.gov/files/pdfs/hyd_economy_bossel_eliasson.pdf.

14 *Hydrogen Production Costs, 2021*, BEIS. Available at assets.publishing.service.gov.uk/government/uploads/system/uploads/attachment_data/file/1011506/Hydrogen_Production_Costs_2021.pdf.

15 Robert Howarth and Mark Jacobson, 'How green is blue hydrogen?', *Energy Science & Engineering* 9:10, 2021, 1676–87.

16 *Work Package 7 Safety Assessment: Conclusions Report*, Hy4Heat/BEIS, May 2021. Available at www.h2knowledgecentre.com/content/project2350.

17 Richard Derwent et al., 'Global environmental impacts of the hydrogen economy', *International Journal of Nuclear Hydrogen Production and Applications* 1:1, 2006, 57–67.

18 *Evaluation of Solid Wall Insulation in Fuel Poor Households in the Private Sector*, Centre for Sustainable Energy, October 2012. Available at www.bathnes.gov.uk/sites/default/files/sitedocuments/Housing/Home-energy-efficiency/evaluation_of_solid_wall_insulation_final_report_october_2012.pdf.

19 Riazat Butt, 'Outrage as council moves to ban tenants' homely doormats', *Guardian*, 14 September 2006, www.theguardian.com/uk/2006/sep/14/communities.homesandgardens.

20 *Warm Homes, Greener Homes: A Strategy for Household Energy Management*, Communities and Local Government/Department for Energy and Climate Change, 2010. Available at www.housinglin.org.uk/_assets/Resources/Housing/OtherOrganisation/warm_homes_greener_homes.pdf.

21 Greg Pitcher, 'Timber tensions: renewing the argument for wood', *Construction News*, 17 May 2022, constructionnews.co.uk/health-and-safety/timber-tensions-renewing-the-argument-for-wood-17-05-2022.

22 Faye Brown, 'Flat owners face £30,000 bill each to replace cladding after Grenfell disaster', *Metro*, 5 October 2020, metro.co.uk/2020/10/05/flat-owners-face-30000-bill-each-to-replace-cladding-after-grenfell-disaster-13368462.

23 *Green Deal and Energy Company Obligation*, National Audit Office, 2016. Available at www.nao.org.uk/wp-content/uploads/2016/04/Green-Deal-and-Energy-Company-Obligation.pdf.

24 Madeleine Cuff, 'Insulation nightmare knocked £100,000 off value of my home – tougher rules are needed to stop rogue traders', *The i*, 25 August 2021, inews.co.uk/news/insulation-value-home-tougher-rules-stop-rogue-traders-1166102.

25 'Damp in social housing blamed on "inappropriate" insulation', BBC News, 28 August 2015, www.bbc.com/news/uk-wales-politics-34081718.

26 Melissa Lawford, 'The great eco con: why homeowners are being punished for going green', *Daily Telegraph*, 20 November 2021.

10. Transport

1 Nick Rufford, 'Transport secretary Grant Shapps on why he bought a Tesla Model 3', *The Times*, 8 September 2019.

2 ourworldindata.org/ghg-emissions-by-sector.

3 'November 2021 new car registrations', Society of Motor Manufacturers and Traders, 6 December 2021, media.smmt. co.uk/november-2021-new-car-registrations.

4 Joanna Partridge, 'Electric cars "will be cheaper to produce than fossil fuel vehicles by 2027"', *Guardian*, 9 May 2021, www.theguardian.com/business/2021/may/09/electric-cars-will-be-cheaper-to-produce-than-fossil-fuel-vehicles-by-2027.

5 Michael Holder, 'Could plummeting battery costs deliver mass market EVs as soon as 2024?', *Investment Week*, 1 December 2021.

6 Matthew Broersma, 'Electric car battery prices rise as lithium costs soar', Silicon UK, 1 November 2021, www.silicon.co.uk/e-innovation/green-it/ev-battery-costs-rise-424279.

7 June Yoon, 'Tesla's reverse on battery cells signals shift for electric vehicles', *Financial Times*, 22 February 2022.

8 Howard Mustoe, 'Why carmakers fear shift to electric could stall', *Daily Telegraph*, 9 March 2022.

9 Daljinder Nagra, 'High upfront costs for electric cars could push more people to petrol', *Which?*, 2 August 2021, www.which.co.uk/news/article/high-upfront-costs-for-electric-cars-could-push-more-people-to-petrol-aniPP0c68lsz.

10 www.nissan.co.uk, November 2020.

11 *Summary: Building a Comprehensive and Competitive Electric Vehicle Charging Sector That Works for All Drivers – Final Report*, Competition and Markets Authority, July 2021. Available at www.gov.uk/government/publications/electric-vehicle-charging-market-study-final-report/final-report.

12 'November 2021 new car registrations'.

13 *Digest of UK Energy Statistics: Annual Data for UK, 2020.*

14 Chris Matthews, 'Owning a car is outdated "20th-century thinking" and we must move to "shared mobility" to cut carbon emissions, transport minister says', *Daily Mail*, 11 December 2021, www.dailymail.co.uk/news/article-10298487/Owning-

car-outdated-20th-century-thinking-transport-minister-
Trudy-Harrison-says.html.

15 *The Location of Development*, Royal Town Planning Institute, December 2021. Available at www.rtpi.org.uk/media/9887/rtpi-location-of-development-final.pdf.

16 Paul Lienert, 'Analysis: When do electric vehicles become cleaner than gasoline cars?', Reuters, 7 July 2021, www.reuters.com/business/autos-transportation/when-do-electric-vehicles-become-cleaner-than-gasoline-cars-2021-06-29.

17 Georg Bieker, *A Global Comparison of the Life-cycle Greenhouse Gas Emissions of Combustion Engine and Electric Passenger Cars*, International Council on Clean Transportation, July 2021. Available at theicct.org/wp-content/uploads/2021/12/Global-LCA-passenger-cars-jul2021_0.pdf.

18 David Cebon, 'Long-haul lorries powered by hydrogen or electricity?', Centre for Sustainable Road Freight blog, 9 February 2020, www.csrf.ac.uk/blog/long-haul-lorries-powered-by-hydrogen-or-electricity.

19 Chirag Panchal, Sascha Stegen and Junwei Lu, 'Review of static and dynamic wireless electric vehicle charging system', *Engineering Science and Technology* 21:5, 2018, 922–37.

20 'New UK study to explore feasibility for dynamic wireless charging for commercial transport', Green Car Congress, 8 June 2021, www.greencarcongress.com/2021/06/20210608-dynamicwpt.html.

21 Mohamad Abou Houran et al., 'Wireless power transfer: Critical review of related standards', paper presented at the 2018 International Power Electronics Conference.

22 *Decarbonising the UK's Long-haul Road Freight at Minimum Economic Cost*, Centre for Sustainable Road Freight, July 2020. Available at www.csrf.ac.uk/wp-content/uploads/2020/11/SRF-WP-UKEMS-v2.pdf.

11. Aviation and shipping

1   *Absolute Zero*, UK FIRES, 2019. Available at www.ukfires.org/wp-content/uploads/2019/11/Absolute-Zero-online.pdf.

2   Tom Bateman, 'Rolls-Royce claims its electric plane is the fastest EV in history', Euronews Next, 23 November 2021, www.euronews.com/next/2021/11/23/rolls-royce-claims-its-electric-plane-is-the-fastest-ev-in-history.

3   'Synthetic fuels in aviation', *Trimis Digest* 13, March 2020, European Commission Joint Research Centre. Available at trimis.ec.europa.eu/sites/default/files/documents/article_1_-_synthetic_fuels.pdf.

4   biofuel.org.uk/north-america.html.

5   'Biofuels from algae', *Postnote* 384, July 2011, Parliamentary Office of Science and Technology. Available at www.parliament.uk/globalassets/documents/post/postpn_384-biofuels-from-algae.pdf.

6   Janina Scheelhaase, Sven Maertens and Wolfgang Grimme, 'Synthetic fuels in aviation – current barriers and potential political measures', *Transportation Research Procedia* 43, 2019, 21–30. Available at elib.dlr.de/140048/1/Scheelhaase_Maertens_Grimme-INAIR_2019_V3.0.pdf.

7   Caspar Henderson, 'The hydrogen revolution in the skies', BBC, 8 April 2021, www.bbc.com/future/article/20210401-the-worlds-first-commercial-hydrogen-plane.

8   *Hydrogen-powered Aviation: A Fact-based Study of Hydrogen Technology, Economics, and Climate Impact by 2050*, Fuel Cells and Hydrogen 2 Joint Undertaking, EU Publications Office, 2020. Available at data.europa.eu/doi/10.2843/471510.

9   Wang Keju, 'More airports in pipeline as travel demand rises', 6 November 2019, english.www.gov.cn/statecouncil/ministries/201911/06/content_WS5dc21f1bc6d0bcf8c4c16a03.html.

10   'China aims to have 450 airports by 2035: aviation regulator',

Reuters, 11 December 2018, www.reuters.com/article/
us-china-economy-aviation-idUSKBN1OA0B4.

11 Andrew Willner, 'New age of sail looks to slash massive
maritime carbon emissions', Mongabay, 15 March 2021, news.
mongabay.com/2021/03/new-age-of-sail-looks-to-slash-
massive-maritime-carbon-emissions.

12 *A Pathway to Decarbonise the Shipping Sector by 2050*, IRENA,
2021. Available at www.irena.org/publications/2021/Oct/A-
Pathway-to-Decarbonise-the-Shipping-Sector-by-2050.

12. Industry

1 Zhiyuan Fan and Julio Friedmann, 'Low-carbon production
of iron and steel: Technology options, economic assessment,
and policy', Columbia School of Public and International
Affairs, March 2021, www.energypolicy.columbia.edu/research/
article/low-carbon-production-iron-steel-technology-options-
economic-assessment-and-policy.

2 Ibid.

3 Interview on *The Andrew Marr Show*, BBC, 7 November 2021.

4 *Pursuing Zero-Carbon Steel in China*, Rocky Mountain Institute,
September 2021. Available at rmi.org/wp-content/uploads/dlm_
uploads/2021/09/Pursuing_Zero_Carbon_Steel_in_China.pdf.

5 *Cement Sector: Industrial Decarbonisation and Energy Efficiency
Roadmap Action Plan*, BEIS, October 2017. Available at
assets.publishing.service.gov.uk/government/uploads/
system/uploads/attachment_data/file/651222/cement-
decarbonisation-action-plan.pdf.

6 Harry Dempsey, 'Decarbonisation to drive "dramatic" rise in
cement prices, says Redburn', *Financial Times*, 27 January 2020.

7 Daniel Posen et al., 'Greenhouse gas mitigation for
U.S. plastics production: energy first, feedstocks later',
Environmental Research Letters 12:3, 2017, iopscience.iop.org/
article/10.1088/1748-9326/aa60a7/pdf.

8 Patricia Nilsson, 'BASF to downsize "permanently" in Europe', *Financial Times*, 26 October 2022.

9 Leigh Krietsch Boerner, 'Industrial ammonia production emits more CO2 than any other chemical-making reaction. Chemists want to change that', *Chemical & Engineering News*, 15 June 2019, cen.acs.org/environment/green-chemistry/Industrial-ammonia-production-emits-CO2/97/i24.

13. Capturing carbon

1 *Planting Trees in England*, National Audit Office, 4 March 2022. Available at www.nao.org.uk/wp-content/uploads/2022/03/Tree-planting-in-England.pdf.

2 Ben Webster, 'Welsh farm dream is lost in investors' carbon credit forest', *The Times*, 5 February 2022.

3 *Greenhouse Gas Removal*, Royal Society and Royal Academy of Engineering, September 2018. Available at royalsociety.org/-/media/policy/projects/greenhouse-gas-removal/royal-society-greenhouse-gas-removal-report-2018.pdf.

4 Niko Kommenda, 'How your flight emits as much CO2 as many people do in a year', *Guardian*, 19 July 2019, www.theguardian.com/environment/ng-interactive/2019/jul/19/carbon-calculator-how-taking-one-flight-emits-as-much-as-many-people-do-in-a-year, quoting German consultancy Atmosfair.

5 'Fact sheet: biochar', American University, Washington DC, 24 June 2020, www.american.edu/sis/centers/carbon-removal/fact-sheet-biochar.cfm.

6 Catherine Keske et al., 'Economic feasibility of biochar and agriculture coproduction from Canadian black spruce forest', *Food and Energy Security* 9:1, February 2020, onlinelibrary.wiley.com/doi/full/10.1002/fes3.188.

7 Nina Friggens et al., 'Tree planting in organic soils does not result in net carbon sequestration on decadal timescales', *Global*

Change Biology 26:9, September 2020, 5178–88, onlinelibrary. wiley.com/doi/full/10.1111/gcb.15229.

8   www.theflowcountry.org.uk/flow-facts/flow-fact-1.

9   '2020 UK Greenhouse Gas Emissions, provisional figures', BEIS, 25 March 2021. Available at assets.publishing.service.gov. uk/government/uploads/system/uploads/attachment_data/ file/972583/2020_Provisional_emissions_statistics_report.pdf.

10   *Energy Technology Perspectives 2020*, IEA. Available at iea.blob.core. windows.net/assets/7f8aed40-89af-4348-be19-c8a67df0b9ea/ Energy_Technology_Perspectives_2020_PDF.pdf.

11   Ibid.

12   Adam Baylin-Stern and Niels Berghout, 'Is carbon capture too expensive?', IEA, 17 February 2021, www.ica.org/ commentaries/is-carbon-capture-too-expensive.

13   'CO2 storage capacity estimation', British Geological Survey, www.bgs.ac.uk/geology-projects/carbon-capture-and-storage/co2-storage-capacity-estimation.

14   Min Jin et al., 'Evaluation of the CO2 storage capacity of the Captain Sandstone formation', paper presented at SPE Europec/EAGE Conference, Copenhagen, June 2012.

15   Gustavo Guariguata-Rojas and John Underhill, 'Implications of Early Cenozoic uplift and fault reactivation for carbon storage in the Moray Firth Basin', *Interpretation, Journal of the Society of Exploration Geophysicists and American Association of Petroleum Geologists* 5:4, November 2017, doi.org/10.1190/ INT-2017-0009.1.

16   Juan Alcalde et al., 'Estimating geological CO2 storage security to deliver on climate mitigation', *Nature Communications* 9, 2018, www.nature.com/articles/s41467-018-04423-1.

17   *Projected Costs of Generating Electricity.*

18   *Gaseous Carbon Waste Streams Utilization: Status and Research Needs*, National Academies of Sciences, Engineering and Medicine, 2019. Available at doi.org/10.17226/25232.

19   *Energy Technology Perspectives 2020.*

14. Agriculture

1   *Agricultural Statistics and Climate Change* (8th edition), DEFRA, 2017. Available at assets.publishing.service.gov.uk/government/uploads/system/uploads/attachment_data/file/666073/agriclimate-8edition-8dec17.pdf.

2   'Huge public support to keep food self-sufficiency levels above 60%', Farming Online, 1 October 2021, www.farming.co.uk/news/huge-public-support-to-keep-food-self-sufficiency-levels-above-60, quoting National Farmers' Union president Minette Batters.

3   *Net Zero Strategy: Build Back Greener.*

4   Hansard, 20 July 2017.

5   *The Sixth Carbon Budget: The UK's Path to Net Zero.*

6   Emma Gatten, 'Vegans use bogus arguments about climate change, says ex-minister leading fight against global warming', *Daily Telegraph*, 29 December 2021.

7   *The Facts about British Red Meat and Milk*, National Farmers' Union, February 2020. Available at www.nfuonline.com/archive?treeid=141504.

8   www.dsm.com/corporate/sustainability/our-purpose/minimizing-methane-from-cattle.html.

9   Breanna Roque, 'Red seaweed (*Asparagopsis taxiformis*) supplementation reduces enteric methane by over 80 percent in beef steers', *Plos One* 16:3, 2021, doi.org/10.1371/journal.pone.0247820.

10 www.ravensdown.co.nz/products/ecopond.

11 'Solar energy and the threat to food security', Net Zero Watch press release, 13 February 2022, www.netzerowatch.com/gargantuan-solar-farms-threaten-uk-farming-and-food-security.

12 Speech to Country Land and Business Association (CLA) Conference, 2 December 2021.

13 'Global vulnerability of crop yields to climate change',

Earth and Environmental Systems Modeling, 21 April 2021, climatemodeling.science.energy.gov/research-highlights/ global-vulnerability-crop-yields-climate-change.

14 Jonas Jägermeyr et al., 'Climate impacts on global agriculture emerge earlier in new generation of climate and crop models', *Nature Food* 2, 2021, 873–85.

15 ourworldindata.org.

16 Dafni Despoina Avgoustaki and George Xydis, 'How energy innovation in indoor vertical farming can improve food security, sustainability, and food safety?', *Advances in Food Security and Sustainability* 5, 2020, doi.org/10.1016/ bs.af2s.2020.08.002.

15. Listen to the scientists

1 Craig Simpson, 'Climate change means outlook is bleak for castle window that confined a king', *Daily Telegraph*, 28 September 2021; 'Planning for a more sustainable future', English Heritage, www.english-heritage.org.uk/visit/inspire-me/smart-energy/ smart-planning.

2 'Climate change could wipe out white Christmases in the UK', BBC Newsround, 7 December 2020, www.bbc.co.uk/ newsround/55212417.

3 Joe Pinkstone, 'How climate change may be making us smaller', *Daily Telegraph*, 8 July 2021.

4 William Rees, 'Yes, the climate crisis may wipe out six billion people', *The Tyee*, 18 September 2019, thetyee.ca/ Analysis/2019/09/18/Climate-Crisis-Wipe-Out.

5 Joe Pinkstone, 'Ketchup at risk from climate change', *Daily Telegraph*, 6 June 2022.

6 Jonathan Chadwick, 'Climate change could spark a rise in KIDNEY STONES: Higher temperatures caused by greenhouse gases will lead to an increase in cases of the painful condition, experts claim', *Daily Mail*, 10 January 2022, www.dailymail.

co.uk/sciencetech/article-10386959/Climate-change-lead-increase-kidney-stones-study-says.html.

7   Damian Carrington, 'Global heating linked to early birth and damage to babies' health, scientists find', *Guardian*, 15 January 2022, www.theguardian.com/environment/2022/jan/15/global-heating-linked-early-birth-damage-babies-health.

8   Severin Carrell, 'Billions needed to protect Glasgow from climate effects, report says', *Guardian*, 29 June 2021, www.theguardian.com/uk-news/2021/jun/29/billions-needed-to-protect-glasgow-from-climate-effects-report-says.

9   Chris Samuel, '"Up to 10,000 excess heatwave deaths" should be anticipated – Ex-Govt Chief Scientist', LBC, 16 July 2022, www.lbc.co.uk/radio/presenters/matt-frei/excess-deaths-heatwave-uk-weather-national-emergency-temperatures-40c.

10   'Excess mortality during heat-periods: 1 June to 31 August 2022', ONS, 7 October 2022, www.ons.gov.uk/peoplepopulationandcommunity/birthsdeathsandmarriages/deaths/articles/excessmortalityduringheatperiods/englandandwales1juneto31august2022.

11   Zainab Hussain, 'England and Wales have seen rise in excess deaths in 2022', *British Medical Journal*, 21 September 2022, doi.org/10.1136/bmj.o2283.

12   'Climate-related mortality and hospital admissions, England and Wales: 2001 to 2020', ONS, January 2022, www.ons.gov.uk/peoplepopulationandcommunity/birthsdeathsandmarriages/deaths/articles/climaterelatedmortalityandhospitaladmissions englandandwales/2001to2020.

13   'Excess winter mortality in England and Wales', ONS, 26 November 2021.

14   Kaya Burgess, *The Times*, 17 January 2022.

15   *UK Climate Change Risk Assessment 2022*, HM Government, 17 January 2022. Available at assets.publishing.service.gov.uk/government/uploads/system/uploads/attachment_data/file/1047003/climate-change-risk-assessment-2022.pdf.

16 *Overheating in New Homes*, Zero Carbon Hub, 2012.

17 Hibaq Farah, 'Plants at risk of extinction as climate crisis disrupts animal migration', *Guardian*, 13 January 2022, www.theguardian.com/environment/2022/jan/13/plants-at-risk-of-extinction-as-climate-crisis-disrupts-animal-migration.

18 Oliver Milman, 'How the speed of climate change is unbalancing the insect world', *Guardian*, 11 January 2022, www.theguardian.com/news/2022/jan/11/climate-change-insect-world-global-heating-species.

19 Maya Wolfe-Robinson, 'Prepare for more extreme weather, Britons warned in wake of Storm Arwen', *Guardian*, 1 December 2021, www.theguardian.com/uk-news/2021/dec/01/storm-arwen-uk-must-prepare-for-more-extreme-weather.

20 'Storm Arwen: Thousands of homes without power for a fourth night', BBC News, 30 November 2021, www.bbc.com/news/uk-england-tyne-59456973.

21 *UK Shared Socioeconomic Pathways*, www.uk-scape.ceh.ac.uk.

22 See, for example, Alys Davies, 'Heatwave engulfs much of Europe as wildfires rage', BBC News, 18 July 2022, www.bbc.com/news/world-europe-62206006.

23 Leo Hickman, 'Exclusive: BBC issues internal guidance on how to report climate change', Carbon Brief, 7 September 2018, www.carbonbrief.org/exclusive-bbc-issues-internal-guidance-on-how-to-report-climate-change.

24 *Today* programme, BBC Radio 4, 22 September 2021.

25 BBC Executive Complaints Unit, 28 April 2022, www.bbc.co.uk/contact/ecu/panorama-wild-weather-bbc-one-3-november-2021.

26 'Humanitarian crisis looms in Madagascar amid drought and pandemic', UN News, 12 January 2021, news.un.org/en/story/2021/01/1081892.

27 Trygve Lavik, 'Climate change denial, freedom of speech and global justice', *Nordic Journal of Applied Ethics* 10:2, 2016,

75–90, www.ntnu.no/ojs/index.php/etikk_i_praksis/article/view/1923/1926.

28 'Your guide to making the climate connection', Covering Climate Now, 14 July 2021, coveringclimatenow.org/resource/your-guide-to-making-the-climate-connection.

29 Tom Knutson, 'Global warming and hurricanes: An overview of current research results', 12 July 2022, www.gfdl.noaa.gov/global-warming-and-hurricanes.

30 *Climate Change 2021: The Physical Science Basis – Sixth Assessment Report of the IPCC*, Chapter 11.

31 Mike Kendon et al., 'State of the UK climate 2021', *International Journal of Climatology* 42:S1, July 2022, 1–80, doi.org/10.1002/joc.7787.

32 *Adapting to Climate Change: UK Climate Projections*, DEFRA, June 2009. Available at assets.publishing.service.gov.uk/government/uploads/system/uploads/attachment_data/file/69257/pb13274-uk-climate-projections-090617.pdf.

33 *Thames Estuary Plan 2100*, Environment Agency, November 2012. Available at assets.publishing.service.gov.uk/government/uploads/system/uploads/attachment_data/file/322061/LIT7540_43858f.pdf.

34 'Thames Estuary 2100: 10-year review monitoring key findings', Environment Agency, 27 September 2022, www.gov.uk/government/publications/thames-estuary-2100-te2100/thames-estuary-2100-key-findings-from-the-monitoring-review.

35 Don Aldiss et al., 'Geological interpretation of current subsidence and uplift in the London area, UK, as shown by high precision satellite-based surveying', *Proceedings of the Geologists' Association* 125:1, January 2014, 1–13.

36 Allison Chinchar, 'Antarctica's last 6 months were the coldest on record', CNN, 9 October 2021, edition.cnn.com/2021/10/09/weather/weather-record-cold-antarctica-climate-change/index.html.

37 Fiona Harvey, 'Heatwaves at both of Earth's poles alarm climate scientists', *Guardian*, 20 March 2022, www.theguardian.com/ environment/2022/mar/20/heatwaves-at-both-of-earth-poles-alarm-climate-scientists.

38 Damien Cave, *The New York Times*, 11 December 2021.

39 *Climate Change 2021: The Physical Science Basis – Sixth Assessment Report of the IPCC*, Chapter 11.

40 Ibid.

41 Ibid.

42 Ibid.

43 Adam Voiland, 'Building a long-term record of fire', NASA Earth Observatory, 20 August 2019, earthobservatory.nasa.gov/ images/145421/building-a-long-term-record-of-fire.

44 www.nifc.gov, accessed 13 November 2018.

45 Quoted in Kate Ramsayer, 'Researchers detect a global drop in fires', NASA Earth Observatory, 29 June 2017, earthobservatory. nasa.gov/images/90493/researchers-detect-a-global-drop-in-fires.

46 Valerie Trouet, 'What turned California forests into a tinderbox? Fire suppression, paradoxically', *Guardian*, 14 September 2020, www.theguardian.com/commentisfree/2020/sep/14/ california-fire-suppression-forests-tinderbox.

47 *Climate Change 2021: The Physical Science Basis – Sixth Assessment Report of the IPCC.*

48 ourworldindata.com.

49 *Climate Change 2021: The Physical Science Basis – Sixth Assessment Report of the IPCC*, Chapter 1.

50 Fred Pearce, 'Claims Himalayan glaciers could melt by 2035 were false, says UN scientist', *Guardian*, 21 January 2010, www.theguardian.com/environment/2010/jan/20/himalayan-glaciers-melt-claims-false-ipcc.

51 Jane Flanagan, 'Staying power of Kilimanjaro snow defies Al Gore's gloomy forecast', *The Times*, 17 February 2020.

16. Green jobs

1   'Renewable energy employment by country', IRENA, www.
    irena.org/statistics/view-data-by-topic/benefits/renewable-
    energy-employment-by-country.

2   'Low carbon and renewable energy economy, UK: 2020',
    ONS, 17 February 2022, www.ons.gov.uk/economy/
    environmentalaccounts/bulletins/finalestimates/2020.

3   *Renewable Energy and Jobs: Annual Review 2021*, IRENA.
    Available at www.irena.org/-/media/files/irena/agency/
    publication/2021/oct/irena_re_jobs_2021.pdf.

4   Veronika Henze, 'Vestas still rules turbine market, but challengers
    are closing in', Bloomberg New Energy Finance, 18 February
    2020, about.bnef.com/blog/vestas-still-rules-turbine-market-
    but-challengers-are-closing-in.

5   Nathalie Thomas and Chris Tighe, 'Why UK pledge to become
    "Saudi Arabia" of wind power rings hollow', *Financial Times*,
    8 January 2021.

6   'Former BiFab yard in Fife to reopen with wind turbine
    contract', BBC News, 16 April 2021, www.bbc.com/news/
    uk-scotland-scotland-business-56769664.

7   'Britishvolt: Electric car battery plant gets millions in
    funding', BBC News, 21 January 2022, www.bbc.com/news/
    business-60066432.

8   'Johnson Matthey announces intention to exit Battery
    Materials and provides trading update', Johnson Matthey, 11
    November 2021, matthey.com/news/2021/battery-materials-
    announcement.

17. Tying ourselves in legal knots

1   'Press summary, R vs Heathrow Airport Ltd', Supreme Court,
    16 December 2020. Available at www.supremecourt.uk/cases/
    docs/uksc-2020-0042-press-summary.pdf.

2   Laurence Fletcher and Derek Brower, 'Hedge funds cash in as green investors dump energy stocks', *Financial Times*, 7 October 2021.

3   'The Netherlands, energy policy review: September 2020', IEA, www.iea.org/reports/the-netherlands-2020.

4   Laura Cola, 'How the Netherlands is turning its back on natural gas', BBC, 27 October 2021, bbc.com/future/article/20211025-netherlands-the-end-of-europes-largest-gas-field.

18. Loading costs on the poor

1   'PM calls on richest countries to meet $100 billion climate pledge', Prime Minister's Office, 10 Downing Street, press release, 20 September 2021, www.gov.uk/government/news/pm-calls-on-richest-countries-to-meet-100-billion-climate-pledge.

2   Thiagarajan Jayaraman, 'Climate and social justice', *UNESCO Courier* 3, 2019, 16–18, doi.org/10.18356/718dd8ac-en.

3   ourworldindata.org.

4   Neel Tamhane, 'Can emerging economies leapfrog the energy transition?', World Economic Forum (WEF), 7 January 2020, www.weforum.org/agenda/2020/01/can-emerging-economies-leapfrog-the-energy-transition.

5   Donald P. Kanak, 'How to replace coal power with renewables in developing countries', WEF, 29 May 2020, www.weforum.org/agenda/2020/05/how-to-replace-coal-and-accelerate-the-energy-transition-in-developing-countries; and 'For health and climate: Retiring coal-fired electricity and promoting sustainable energy transition in developing countries', Program on International Financial Systems, 12 August 2020, www.pifsinternational.org/wp-content/uploads/2022/09/Coal-retirement-mechanism-v10.1-full-length-1.pdf.

6   'Hurricane Ian blunts strong autumn demand for bizjets in US', WingX report, BlueSky News, 6 October 2022,

www.blueskynews.aero/issue-672/WINGX-Global-Market-Tracker-061022.html.

7 'Air traffic recovery is fast-approaching pre-pandemic levels', International Civil Aviation Organization, 19 September 2022, www.icao.int/Newsroom/Pages/Air-traffic-recovery-is-fastapproaching-prepandemic-levels.aspx.

8 Philip Georgiadis and Sylvia Pfeifer, 'Private jet rush prompts plane shortage as rich dodge airline woes', *Financial Times*, 16 November 2021.

9 Kate Abnett, 'Draft shows EU to propose aviation fuel tax in green policy push', Reuters, 5 July 2021, www.reuters.com/business/sustainable-business/draft-shows-eu-propose-aviation-fuel-tax-green-policy-push-2021-07-04.

10 *Climate Impacts of Exemptions to EU's Shipping Proposals*, Transport & Environment, January 2022. Available at www.transportenvironment.org/wp-content/uploads/2022/01/Climate_Impacts_of_Shipping_Exemptions_Report-1.pdf.

11 Damian Carrington, 'UN global climate poll: "The people's voice is clear – they want action"', *Guardian*, 27 January 2021, www.theguardian.com/environment/2021/jan/27/un-global-climate-poll-peoples-voice-is-clear-they-want-action.

12 'YouGov Cambridge survey results', YouGov, October 2021. Available at docs.cdn.yougov.com/2ktwn4762t/YouGov%20Cambridge%20European%20Environmental%20inc%20COP26.pdf.

13 'YouGov – COP26 support, effective, willing (initial release)', YouGov, October 2021. Available at docs.cdn.yougov.com/dynh8rffto/YouGov%20-%20COP26%20initial%20release.pdf.

14 'Fuel duty rates, 1988–2021', Institute for Government, www.instituteforgovernment.org.uk/charts/fuel-duty-rates.

15 *National Diet and Nutrition Survey: Diet, Nutrition and Physical Activity in 2020*, Public Health England and the Food Standards Agency, September 2021. Available at

assets.publishing.service.gov.uk/government/uploads/
system/uploads/attachment_data/file/1019663/Follow_up_
stud_2020_main_report.pdf.

16 Douglas Broom, '1 in 7 people would choose not to fly because
of climate change', 30 August 2019, WEF, www.weforum.
org/agenda/2019/08/1-in-7-people-would-choose-not-to-
fly-because-of-climate-change.

17 'Organic food is more expensive than non-organic, survey
finds', DJS Research, 1 February 2016, www.djsresearch.
co.uk/RetailMarketResearchInsightsAndFindings/article/
Organic-food-is-more-expensive-than-non-organic-survey-
finds-02918.

18 'Average household income, UK: financial year ending
2021', ONS, 28 March 2022, www.ons.gov.uk/-
peoplepopulationandcommunity/personalandhouseholdfinances/
incomeandwealth/bulletins/householddisposableincomeand-
inequality/financialyearending2021.

19 'Green party to join national demonstration against government
austerity', Green Party, 20 June 2014, www.greenparty.
org.uk/news/2014/06/20/green-party-to-join-national-
demonstration-against-government-austerity.

20 Letter to the *Guardian*, 20 April 2021, www.theguardian.com/
environment/2021/apr/23/endless-pursuit-of-economic-
growth-is-destroying-our-planet.

19. So what should we do?

1 ourworldindata.org.

2 *Shale Gas Extraction in the UK*.

3 'Government ends support for fracking', BEIS press release,
2 November 2019, www.gov.uk/government/news/government-
ends-support-for-fracking.

4 Selina Roman-White et al., *Life Cycle Greenhouse Gas Perspective
on Exporting Liquefied Natural Gas from the United States: 2019*

Update, National Energy Technology Laboratory, 12 September 2019. Available at www.energy.gov/sites/prod/files/2019/09/f66/2019%20NETL%20LCA-GHG%20Report.pdf.

5 miraigroup.jp/en.

6 *Managing the Coast in a Changing Climate*, Climate Change Committee, October 2018. Available at www.theccc.org.uk/wp-content/uploads/2018/10/Managing-the-coast-in-a-changing-climate-October-2018.pdf.

7 Victoria Seabrook, 'Climate change causing Britain to shrink with some coastal communities condemned to be swallowed by the sea', Sky News, 7 June 2022, news.sky.com/story/climate-change-causing-britain-to-shrink-with-some-coastal-communities-condemned-to-be-swallowed-by-the-sea-12628943.

8 Luke Murphy, Joshua Emden and Henry Parkes, 'The Chancellor's energy plan is a sticking plaster full of holes', Institute for Public Policy Research, 3 February 2022, www.ippr.org/blog/energy-crisis-support-analysis.

9 dezandmotor.nl/en.

10 global.royalhaskoningdhv.com/projects/a-uk-first-sandscaping-building-with-nature-in-bacton-norfolk.

11 Grace Newcombe, *Plain Dealing: Building for Flood Resilience*, Localis, November 2021. Available at www.localis.org.uk/wp-content/uploads/2021/11/042_Floodplains_WebAWK.pdf.

12 'Beavers in Essex doing "better job" of making flood defences', BBC News, 21 May 2019, www.bbc.com/news/uk-england-essex-48342951.

13 Hannah Cloke, 'Climate change means we won't in future be able to engineer our way out of flooding', *Guardian*, 11 February 2014, www.theguardian.com/commentisfree/2014/feb/11/climate-change-flooding-engineer-somerset.

14 *Flood and Coastal Erosion Risk Management Strategy: Roadmap to 2026*, Environment Agency, 7 June 2022. Available at

assets.publishing.service.gov.uk/government/uploads/system/
uploads/attachment_data/file/1080740/FCERM-Strategy-
Roadmap-to-2026-FINAL.pdf.

15 'Key findings of the Pentagon', *Observer*, 22 February 2004,
www.theguardian.com/environment/2004/feb/22/usnews.
theobserver1.

16 Juan Lora, Jonathan Mitchell and Aradhna Tripati, 'Abrupt
reorganization of North Pacific and western North American
climate during the last deglaciation', *Geophysical Research Letters*
43:22, 2016, doi.org/10.1002/2016GL071244.

Index

California 154
California, University of 155
Cambridgeshire 82, 156, 234
Cameroon 144
Canada 154, 180
Captain Sandstone 144
Carbon Border Adjustment Mechanism
   130
carbon capture 136–47
   Biden's tax credits 36
   industrial processes 141–7
   Network Rail's trees 2
   Russia 27
   trees 2, 136–41
carbon capture and storage (CCS)
   86
Carbon Capture, Utilisation and
   Storage plants (CCUSs) 142–7
carbon dioxide
   atmospheric concentration 179
   Britain 39
   capture of 142, 146
   cement 127
   China 19, 20
   fuel emissions 30, 34
   hydrogen free of 86
   increase 5
   lignite 34
   plants and 160
   removing 10
   Russia 27
   steel 127–8
   underground leakage 144
   wind-powered electricity grid
      emissions 67
   woodburning 45
carbon emissions
   Britain 5, 40
   China 3, 19, 20, 22–3
   coal, gas and 30, 34
   counting methods 226
   Russia 24, 33
   technology and 7
   United States 36
   see also decarbonising
Cardiff 68
Carmarthenshire 137–8

cars
   batteries 194 see also batteries
   becoming a luxury 114
   carless society 106–7
   running costs 212
   sale statistics 99
   see also diesel cars; electric cars;
      petrol cars
cash payments 4–5
cattle 148–9, 151, 153–6
cavity wall insulation 80
cement 12, 127, 131–2, 138, 145
Central London 177 see also London
Centre for Sustainable Energy 92
Centre for Sustainable Road Freight
   110, 112
CF Fertilisers 134
Channel Islands 51
Chatham House 45
Chernobyl 71, 74–5
Chester 135
Chicago 117
Chicago Convention (1944) 115
China 17–23
   aviation industry 123
   'Blue Book' 18
   climate change, reaction to 15, 18,
      20, 22–3
   coal 4, 208
   COP26 absentee 3
   economic growth, importance of 8
   floods 17–18
   green jobs 191
   greenhouse gas percentages 34
   lithium carbonate prices 100
   net zero commitment 18–19, 22
   SMRs 76
   steel 40, 130–1
   Yellow River 182
China Meteorological Administration
   Association 18
Chrysler Crossfires 98
ClientEarth 198, 200
climate change
   activists and campaigners' influence
      8
   benefits from 165
   Britain on its own 15

INDEX

food production
  cost of to poorer people 212–13
  crop yields 158–60
  diet changing 152
  food security 157–8, 225
  UK self-sufficiency 149–50
  woodland and 13, 137
Food Strategy (UK Government) 151
Forest Research 139
forestry 46 *see also* woodland
fossil fuels
  carbon dioxide and 5
  China 21
  EU imports from Russia 28
  Europe neglects 214
  hydrogen production 86
  phasing out and phasing down 4–5
  2021 UK figures 43, 44
  see also carbon dioxide; coal;
    electricity: Britain: comparative
    costs; gas, greenhouse gases
fracking 29–30, 223–4
France
  electricity prices 40, 193
  gilets jaunes 210
  Jersey dispute 66
  national grid link 64–5
  net zero commitment 19
  nuclear energy 76–7
  wildfires 5
Fraserburgh 167
Friends of the Earth 197, 200
Fukushima 34, 71, 75, 77
furnaces 128–30
fusion plants 72

gas
  Britain's self-sufficiency 29
  carbon dioxide and 30, 34
  China 19, 20, 21–2
  closer to home options 223–5
  closures 44, 201–2
  electricity and 52
  European production 28
  hydrogen might replace 13
  India's position 4
  intermittency of renewable energy
    and 55–9

liquified natural gas (LNG) 29
  prices 88
  Russian 25–7, 214
  shale gas 29–30
  switch from coal 28, 35, 39
  see also electricity: Britain:
    comparative costs
gas boilers 13, 44, 78–9
Gasland (Josh Fox) 30
GDP 11, 20–1
General Assembly, UN 19
genetic modification (GM) 159
Germany
  Aerospace Center 119
  electric car charging 111
  electricity prices 40, 193
  energy storage 61
  net zero target 28, 34–5
  nuclear power 77
  Passivhaus 91
  U-boats 157
  weaning itself from Russian gas 25
  wind turbine production 194
Gijón 129
gilets jaunes 210
Gironde department 5
Glasgow 162
global warming *see* temperatures
Goddard Space Flight Center (NASA)
  184
Good Law Project 198–9
Gore, Al 169, 187
Gotland 111
Gove, Michael 152
Great Ouse, River 234
Green Deal 94, 95
green hydrogen 86–9, 110, 129–30
  see also hydrogen
green jobs 191–2, 205
Green Party 215
greenhouse gas emissions
  agriculture 149
  Britain 9–10, 38–9
  four biggest emitters 34
  from woodburning 46
  hydrogen as 90–1
  imports do not count 137
  increasing 186

275

North America 45–6, 66, 182, 238
North East (England) 191
North Norfolk District Council 228
North Sea
  carbon dioxide 144
  Europe stops developing 28, 29, 223
  Morocco and 65
  storing hydrogen 62
Northamptonshire 174
Northumberland 167, 194
Norway 29, 65, 66, 108
Nottingham 81
nuclear energy 71–7
  electricity and 49
  fission 71
  fusion 42, 72–3, 221–2
nuclear power stations 12–13, 25–6, 34
nuclear weapons 24
Nyos, Lake 144

Observer 236
O'Connor, Ian 137
Odey, Crispin 201
OECD 204
Office for National Statistics (ONS)
  163–5
Ofgem 55, 82
oil 4, 20, 21–2, 201, 214
oil-fired boilers 78–9
Old Testament 218
oligarchs (Russian) 25
Opinium poll 78–9
Orbital O2 turbines 69
Orkney 69
Our World in Data 219

Pacific 183
Pacific Northwest National Laboratory
  62
Panorama (BBC) 170
Paris 177
Paris Agreement 19, 35, 197–8, 200,
  203
Parrett, River 233
particulates 47–8
Passivhaus 91
peat bogs 13, 140–1, 150
Pentagon 236

personal protective equipment (PPE)
  133
Petra Nova plant, Texas 143
petrol cars 13, 44, 98, 101–3, 108
Peugeot 208 101–3
'phasing down' 4
photovoltaic power 21
Piper planes 116
Plan B Earth 197
planes *see* aviation
plastics 133
Plymouth, University of 50–1
PM2.5s 47
pollution 19, 47–8, 131
population figures 219
Pripyat, Ukraine 74
private jets 2
protectionism 36
Public Accounts Committee (House of
  Commons) 83
Public Health England 211
public transport 107
pumped storage systems 58–9
Putin, Vladimir 3, 24–8, 31

Qatar 29, 224
Queensland 182

Radio 4 (BBC) 169
railways 113
rainfall 17, 18, 175–6, 179–80, 186
Ravensdown 155
Redburn 132
Ren Guoyu 18
renewable energy
  China 18
  not yet zero carbon 67
  overtaking fossil fuels? 43, 44–5,
    48–9
  potential amount of 50
  practical requirements 195–6
  see also electricity: Britain;
    comparative costs; solar power;
    wind power
Renewable Energy Directive (EU) 119
Renewable Heat Incentive (RHI) 47
Renewables Obligation 55
RenewableUK 193